THE FIRST X-MEN™

Children of the Atom

WRITERS: NEAL ADAMS & CHRISTOS GAGE
PENCILS: NEAL ADAMS
INKS: NEAL ADAMS & ANDREW CURRIE

COLOURIST: MATTHEW WILSON
LETTERS: VIRTUAL CALLIGRAPHY'S CLAYTON COWLES
ASSISTANT EDITOR: JORDAN D WHITE

EDITOR: NICK LOWE
EDITOR-IN-CHIEF: AXEL ALONSO
CHIEF CREATIVE OFFICER: JOE QUESADA
EXECUTIVE PRODUCER: ALAN FINE
PUBLISHER: DAN BUCKLEY
COVER ART: NEAL ADAMS
COVER COLOURS: MATTHEW WILSON

o you have any comments or queries about this graphic novel?
nail us at graphicnovels@panini.co.uk

MARVEL www.marvel.com

MARVEL GRAPHIC NOVEL

FIRST X-MEN #

HARLEM. MANY YEARS AGO.
IT'S HARD TO TURN
OWN A FRIEND ASKING
FAVOR. WHICH IS WHY
MAKE IT A POINT NOT
TO HAVE FRIENDS.
BUT SOMETIMES IT CAN'T BE HELPED.
OLD WAR BUDDY ASKED ME TO FIND HIS SON. KID RAN OFF. MOST PEOPLE THOUGHT DRUGS, BUT HE KNEW DIFFERENT.
THINGS HAVE BEEN GOING ON WITH THE KID LATELY. "YOUR KINDA THINGS," IS HOW HE PUT IT.
SNIFF SNIFF
I'M A PRIVATE GUY. BUT SPEND TIME AROUND ME IN COMBAT AND YOU CAN'T HELP BUT NOTICE I'M NOT YOUR TYPICAL GRUNT.
HE THINKS HIS SON MIGHT BE LIKE ME. DIFFERENT. AND THAT HE MIGHT NEED HELP.
IF HE'S ANYTHING LIKE ME, DAMN RIGHT HE DOES.
THERE.
ANTHONY?
ME'S LOGAN.
A FRIEND O'
YOUR DAD.
I KNOW YOU'RE SCARED. I KNOW YOU'RE HURTING. I CAN HELP.
ANTHONY?
YOU CAN'T HELP ME.

HEY!
HEY, MAN, YOU DEAD?
WHUH!
I'M FINE. KNOCKED THE WIND OUTTA ME, IS ALL.
DAMN, SON, I THOUGHT YOU WAS MESSED UP! I C'N CALL EMERGENCY--
DON'T BOTHER. JUST SCRATCHED UP.
LITTLE BIT CLOSER AND YOU'D BE SHREDDED LIKE THEM. GAS MAIN, MUST BE.
GAS MAIN, HUH?
YOU WAS LUCKY, BRO.
YEAH, LUCKY.

THE CENTRAL PARK ZOO.
DON'T NEED ENHANCED SENSES TO SMELL FEDS.
ZIPPED THE POOR KID UP IN A BODYBAG THEN LIT OUT.
FAST AS THEY GOT THERE, THEY WERE ALREADY LOOKING FOR HIM. SPEED THEY WORKED AT... THEY'VE DONE IT BEFORE.
SO?
IT'S FINALLY HAPPENED, CREED.
THE GOVERNMENT'S HUNTING PEOPLE LIKE US.
IT'S ILLEGAL TO BE A BASTARD NOW?
I AIN'T LAUGHIN'. YOU'VE SEEN WHAT I HAVE THE PAST COUPLE YEARS... MORE AND MORE LIKE US SHOWIN' UP.
KIDS, MOST OF 'EM. ODDS ARE THEY'LL END UP LIKE ANTHONY. OR WORSE... LAB RATS. CUT OPEN TO SEE WHAT MAKES 'EM WORK.
YEAH, IT'S A HARD WORLD. I SAY AGAIN: SO?
SO THESE KIDS NEED SOMEONE ON THEIR SIDE. SOMEONE LIKE THEM. FIGURE THAT'S ME.
FIGURE THAT'S YOU, TOO.

YOU SON OF A--
I CAME HERE 'CAUSE I THOUGHT YOU HAD A JOB.
WE'RE HIRED KILLERS, NOT SOCIAL WORKERS. WHY THE HELL WOULD I WASTE TWO DAMN SECONDS ON YOUR TOUCHY-FEELY CRAP?
ONE: I'LL PAY YOU.
TWO: NO ONE ELSE IS DOING IT. AND THREE...
...WHAT IF THERE'D BEEN SOMEONE WHO GAVE A DAMN WHEN YOU WERE A KID?
DADDY, NO! I'LL BE GOOD! I PROMISE!
PLEEEEASE!
YOU'LL PAY ME HOW MUCH?

QUANTICO, VIRGINIA.
I KNOW YOU CALLED IN FAVORS TO FIND THIS PLACE, BUT IT LOOKS PRETTY ORDINARY TO ME. YOU SURE THIS IS IT?
I GOT A SCENT.
A FAMILIAR ONE. NOW SHUT UP AND MOVE.

ANTHONY.
BASTARDS.
I BET MY LAST DIME THEY DON'T JUST DO THAT TO THE DEAD ONES.
SSSLKTT
THEY AIN'T GONNA DO IT TO ANYONE EVER AGAIN.

WE NEED TO KNOW WHO THEY'RE AFTER. GET TO 'EM FIRST.
SOUNDS GOOD.

LET'S SEE WHAT'S SO IMPORTANT THEY KEEP IT LOCKED AWAY EVEN FROM THEIR OWN PEOPLE.

PAYDIRT. ES ON PEOPLE Y'RE WATCHIN'. ANDIDATES.
HOLD IT.
THIS FEELS WRONG.
EVEN THIS LATE, THERE SHOULD BE *SOMEONE* HERE... NIGHT WATCHMEN. YOU SMELL ANY?
JUST MACHINERY.
BUT NOT MEDICAL EQUIPMENT. MORE LIKE... A *TANK*...
DOWN!
SHZZATT
I'LL BE DAMNED. THOUGHT IT WAS COMMIE AGENTS, BUT IT'S LOGAN AND CREED!
HA! THEY WALTZED RIGHT IN THE FRONT DOOR!

BRASS'S BEEN LOOKING FOR YOU TWO. AWFUL CONSIDERATE TO SAVE US THE LEGWORK.
I'LL HACK YOUR LEGS OF AND SHOVE 'EM UP YOUR--
SHHZZ
GRRAAAGGH!
RARRR-- YOU...
KZZTTT
WE KNOW ABOUT YOU, TOUGH GUYS. YOU MIGHT HEAL FAST, BUT YOU STILL FEEL PAIN. AND ENOUGH PAIN PUTS DOWN ANY ANIMAL.
...KNOW...
STHTT
...NOTHING...
SNIKT
...ABOUT ME!
SON OF A--!

SHHKK
OH MY GOD!
PULL YOURSELF TOGETHER, CARLSON! WE'VE GOT 'EM OUT--
HRRAAARRR!
--GUNNED...
EEAAAGHHH!
THE FILES. YOU GET WHAT YOU NEEDED?
IT'S ENOUGH. LET'S GET THE HELL OUT OF HERE.

"NOTHIN' BACK THERE BUT DEATH."
H...HELLO...?
THEY KNEW US, LOGAN. HOW THE HELL DO THEY KNOW US?
WE BEEN KICKIN' AROUND AWHILE. I AIN'T SURPRISED.
DON'T MATTER. WE CAN TAKE CARE OF OURSELVES. THESE KIDS CAN'T.
WE GOTTA FIGURE OUT WHO THE TOP TARGETS ARE AND--
AH, CRAP.
WHAT?
I JUST FIGURED OUT WHY THEY'RE UNDERSTAFFED. EIGHTEEN-YEAR-OLD KID NAMED HOLLY BRIGHT, IN D.C. A RUNAWAY.
THEY'RE MOVING ON HER TONIGHT.
THE CAPITAL? THAT'S ABOUT THIRTY FIVE MILES FROM HERE
WELL, HERE'S OUR RIDE.

ASHINGTON, D.C.
IT'S ALL THERE, LADY. PLEASE...
I NEED THIS.
YOU DON'T KNOW HOW LONG I'VE WAITED...
ALL RIGHT, KEEP IT DOWN. FOLLOW ME.
THAT'S HOLLY BRIGHT? YOU'D THINK A BROAD THAT FINE COULD DO BETTER'N TURNING TRICKS IN AN ALLEY.
SHE'S LIKE US. AND WE'VE DONE A LOT WORSE TO SURVIVE.
C'MON.
HE HELL IS--?
HH.
OH, GOD, BABY...

I JUST KEEP THINKING... IF I HADN'T HAD SO MUCH TO DRINK MAYBE I'D HAVE WOKEN UP... SMELLED THE SMOKE... HEARD YOU SCREAMING...
IT'S OKAY, DADDY. I KNOW MOMMY BLAMES YOU, BUT I DON'T.
I FORGIVE YOU. IT DOESN'T HURT ANYMORE.
SHFFLE
WHO THER
WHAT THE HELL YOU WANT
TO HELP.
I'M WITH A CLIENT. COME BACK LATER, I'LL MAKE YOUR DREAM COME TRUE. BET IT HAS TO DO WITH BEING TALLER THAN A GARDEN GNOME.
HEH. EASY, LEGS. WE AIN'T THE BAD GUYS.
BUT IF YOU DON'T LOSE THE ATTITUDE--
ME? YOU'RE THREATENING ME?
DAMN IT. I WARNED YOU.
YOU ARE ALL UNDER ARREST. GET ON YOUR KNEES AND PUT YOUR HANDS BEHIND YOUR HEAD.
ALL UNITS, LETHAL FORCE AUTHORIZED. REPEAT, AT THE FIRST SIGN OF RESISTANCE, LETHAL FORCE IS AUTHORIZED.

MUSIC TO MY EARS.
SNIKT
GGRRAAA!
C'MERE, YOU.
SHRRNNKK
YOU STILL HERE, HOLLY? WHAT THE HELL'S WRONG WITH YOU? GET AWAY!
RUN FOR YOUR DAMN LIFE!
I'VE DONE THAT ENOUGH.
I THINK THEY SHOULD RUN.

OH MY DEAR GOD!
OH, NO!

EVASIVE ACTION!
LOOK OUT FOR THE ROTORS!
BAIL! BAIL! BAIL!
SHRAKOOOM
WHAT THE HELL IS THAT THING?
DID YOU BRING THAT THING? OR MAKE IT?
WHUFF!
HNH. LIGHTER' THOUG
PRETTY IMPRESSIVE, GIRL. I COULD SMELL THAT THING.
IT'S WHAT I DO. GET IN YOUR HEAD. MAKE IT SEEM REAL.
NOT R ENOU
WHAT D YOU REA LOOK LI
CALL ME HOLO. THIS IS WHAT I LOOK LIKE.
DON'T MATTER TO ME. BUT I'M LESS LIKELY TO WRAP US AROUND A TREE ALLOWIN' FOR YOUR REAL WEIGHT.
FINE.
DAMN!

DISAPPOINTED?
NOT MINE TO SAY, KID. I GO FOR WOMEN, NOT JAILBAIT.
YOU'RE GOOD, KID. THINK YOU CAN MAKE PEOPLE SEE FAKE PASSPORTS?
CAUSE THE NEXT NAME ON THIS LIST AIN'T IN DRIVING DISTANCE."
OXFORD UNIVERSITY.
I KNOW HE WAS HORRIBLE TO YOU, BUT THAT WAS AGES AGO. PERHAPS THE ARMY'S MADE HIM GROW UP. OCH, LOVE, HE'S YUIR BROTHER.
STEP-BROTHER. AND BELIEVE ME, MOIRA, YOU DO NOT WANT HIM AT OUR WEDDING.
CHARLES? IS SOMETHING WRONG?
I...JUST REMEMBERED, I NEED TO SPEAK TO PROFESSOR FLETCHER. GO ON AHEAD.
CHARLES FRANCIS XAVIER, YOU CAN LOOK SO BLOODY SERIOUS AT TIMES.
YOU'D THINK DEATH HIMSELF 'AD COME FOR YOU!
ALL RIGHT, WHO ARE YOU PEOPLE? WHY ARE YOU FOLLOWING ME?
I'VE TAILED COMBAT VETERANS WHO NEVER CAUGHT WIND'A ME. HOW'D YOU?
THAT BOY YOU'RE CARRYING... IS HE--

DEAD? DAMN STRAIGHT.
THEY'RE COMIN' FOR US. MAYBE IT AIN'T HAPPENED HERE YET, BUT IT WILL.
I...HAVE NO IDEA WHAT YOU--
SHUT UP.
WE'RE GRUNTS...FIGHTERS. YOU'RE SOME KINDA GENIUS. AND YOU GOT MORE'N JUST SMARTS. WE NEED SOMEONE LIKE--
WAIT. THIS BOY IS A... A FIGMENT. AN ILLUSION.
HE WAS REAL. NOW HE'S GONE. WITH YOUR HELP, WE MIGHT'A REACHED HIM IN TIME TO SAVE HIM.
YOUR PEOPLE NEED YA, KID.
MY... "PEOPLE?"
YOU HAVE NOTHING TO DO WITH ME. NOR I WITH YOU.
KEEP TELLIN' YOURSELF THAT.
YOU BEEN FLAGGED, KID. GRADUATIN' HARVARD AT SIXTEEN, THREE Ph.DS BY EIGHTEEN...
ALL RIGHT, YES, I'M... SMART. A LOT OF PEOPLE ARE.

I DON'T NEED TO READ MINDS TO KNOW YOU AND THAT... CREATURE BEHIND YOU ARE NOTHING LIKE ME.
I'M ENGAGED! I HAVE A FUTURE! I AM GOING TO GET MARRIED, HAVE CHILDREN AND LIVE A HAPPY, BORING PROFESSOR'S LIFE!
YOU DO THAT, YOU'LL LIVE IT HEARIN' THE SCREAMS'A DYIN' KIDS IN YOUR HEAD.
ENOUGH! LEAVE ME BE!
AND ON THE DAY YOU DIE, THE LAST THING YOU'LL HEAR IS THE VOICES'A ALL THOSE SOULS YOU COULDA HELPED...
...AND DIDN'T.
ON THE DAY I DIE, IT WILL BE AS A HUMAN BEING!
UH-HUH.
Y'KNOW THAT LAST THING I SAID?
DIDN'T SAY IT OUT LOUD.
YOU NEED TO GET A LOT BETTER AT HIDIN' IN PLAIN SIGHT, KID.
CHARMIN' AS EVER. HAD LITTLE LORD FAUNTLEROY EATIN' OUTTA YER HAND.
HELL WITH HIM. TYPICAL RICH KID. NOTHIN' BUT A COWARD...AN' A QUITTER.
MOIRA? WE HAVE TO TALK.
YES...I'M AFRAID IT IS SERIOUS.

"SO WHAT NOW, LOGAN?"
"I GOT A LINE ON A BETTER PROSPECT. NEXT STOP, ARGENTINA."
P-PLEASE.. I WAS ONL DOING MY DU SERVING M COUNTRY..
"HE'S A MAN NOT A BOY. BE THROUGH HEL AND BACK.
YES. YOU SERVED YOUR FÜHRER WELL, HERR HORST. AND YOU SHOULD BE RECOGNIZED...
...WITH A CHEST FULL OF MEDALS.
N-NO...
SHLKK
THANK YOU, GENTLEMEN...IT HAS BEEN A MOST STIMULATING DAY.
"AND HE'S BEEN BLOODED.
"NAME'S ERIK LEHNSHERR."

COLORADO.
I SWEAR ON MY KIDS, IT WAS BIGFOOT. HAD TO BE EIGHT FEET TALL. HE CAME TO A LOG BLOCKING HIS WAY AND DEMOLISHED IT WITH ONE SWIPE'A HIS HAND.
LIKE YOU JUST DEMOLISHED A TWELVE-PACK, RIGHT, STU?
SHUT UP.
MY ANIMALS'VE BEEN ACTIN' UP ALL DAY. SOMETHING'S OUT THERE. PROB'LY JUST A BEAR, BUT THEY'LL KILL YA AS DEAD AS A YETI.
YETIS COME FROM THE HIMALAYAS, RAY.
I'LL SMACK YOU SO HARD YOU'LL THINK YOU'RE IN THE HIMALAYAS IF YOU DON'T SHUT UP.
AFTERNOON.
I DON'T SUPPOSE ANY OF YOU FELLAS COULD GIVE ME A RIDE EAST?
LORD HAVE MERCY...

KILL IT!
OH, COME ON! NOT AGAIN!
--YUHH!
B-BLAM BLAM
IT'S DOWN! FINISH IT--
--OFF?
SHNKK

HURRRAAAGGHH
OHMYGODRUN!

SHUT UP!
HEY, PICK ONE LOOK AND STICK TO IT.
THANKS. I DIDN'T WANT TO HURT THOSE FELLAS. I WAS JUST LOOKING FOR A RIDE.
HERE'S A TIP. DON'T JUMP OUT AT GUYS WITH GUNS. 'SPECIALLY WHEN YOU LOOK LIKE A GRIZZLY.
WE BEEN TRACKIN' YOU SINCE THE SIERRA NEVADA. SEEMS LIKE YOU'RE A MAN WITH A MISSION.
WHERE YOU HEADED? MAYBE WE CAN HELP YA OUT.

FIGURE WE NEED TO STICK TOGETHER. BE READY FOR 'EM. AND WHEN WE'RE UP TO IT, TAKE THE FIGHT TO THEM.
WHAT HAPPENED TO YER BROTHER?
HE'S...LIKE US. DIFFERENT. SPECIAL. OLDER THAN ME, BUT HIS MIND...HE'S LIKE A LITTLE KID.

HE'S ALIVE. I CAN FEEL IT. WE HAVE A CONNECTION.

YOU OKAY, KID?
FINE... I'M PRETTY TOUGH.
WAS THAT THE MANPHIBIAN?
I LIKED THAT MOVIE.
WHY THE HELL WOULD A FISH BE IN THE WOODS?

TRACKING ME?
IF YOU'RE WITH THE FEDS WHO TOOK MY BROTHER--
EASY, PAL. WE'RE LIKE YOU. THOSE FEDS ARE AFTER US, TOO.
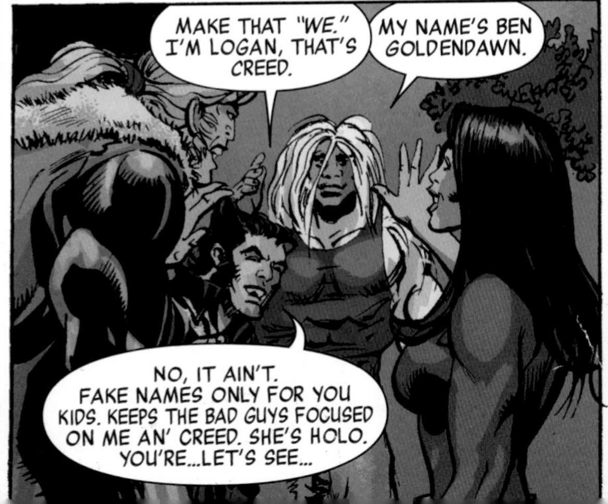
MAKE THAT "WE." I'M LOGAN, THAT'S CREED.
MY NAME'S BEN GOLDENDAWN.
NO, IT AIN'T. FAKE NAMES ONLY FOR YOU KIDS. KEEPS THE BAD GUYS FOCUSED ON ME AN' CREED. SHE'S HOLO. YOU'RE...LET'S SEE...

WHAT THAT REDNECK CALLED HIM. YETI.
YETIS COME FROM THE HIMALAYAS.
SHUT UP.
ALL'A YOU SHUT UP.

QUANTICO, VIRGINIA.
TYPICAL FEDS. SOON AS WE COMPROMISED THEIR SECURITY, THEY TOOK OFF.
IN A HURRY. SMELL THAT? DECOMPOSITION.
THEY SHOVED ALL THEIR TRAS IN A HOLE AND BUR IT. YETI, YOU AS STRONG AS YOU LOOK?
STRONGER. I'LL HAVE IT DUG UP IN NO TIME.
LOOK OUT!

I THINK ERE'S SOMEONE ALIVE IN THERE.
TOR-- U'RE RT!
IT'S NOTHIN'. JUST A LITTLE SHRAPNEL.
BUT YOU WERE PROTECTING *ME...*

HELLO? PLEASE...
...I NEED HELP...
ANTHONY?

MY BROTHER'S NOT DOWN THERE. I STILL FEEL HIM. HE'S *ALIVE.*
SEE? ALL BETTER.
I SAW YOU *DIE!* BLOW YOURSELF UP!
THAT'S WHAT *THEY* THOUGHT. BUT WHEN YOU CUT ME LOOSE FROM THEIR MACHINES, I STARTED TO HEAL.

I COULD HEAR 'EM FREAKING OUT. THEY WERE PACKING UP. BURYING THE DEAD. TRIED TO TELL 'EM I WAS ALIVE...BUT I WAS TOO WEAK.

I HEARD YOUR VOICES. KNEW I HAD TO GET OUT...OR DIE.

LOOK, KID. I'M SURE IF THEY KNEW YOU WERE ALIVE, THEY WOULD'VE...YOU KNOW...BUT LOOK AT YOU.

YOU DIRECTED THE BLAST *UP.* CONTROLLED IT BETTER THAN LAST TIME.

I...GUESS. I JUST KNEW I NEEDED OUT. DIDN'T REALLY THINK ABOUT HOW.

WELL, YER GONNA START.
IF THEY LEFT ALL THESE TEST SUBJECTS BEHIND, IT MEANS THEY GOT A LINE ON MORE.
SOON AS THEY GET SET UP SOMEWHERE ELSE, THEY'LL LOOK TO STOCK UP.
BUT WE'RE GONNA BE READY.
C'MON, ALL'A YA. REVEILLE'S AT 0600.
UPSTATE NEW YORK.
NICE SPREAD, LOGAN. NEVER KNEW YOU HAD THIS.
'CAUSE I DIDN'T TELL YA, CREED.
ALWAYS FIGURED I'D COME HERE WHEN THE KILLIN' WAS DONE. JUST GET LOST AND STAY THAT WAY.
NICE IDEA. ONE PROBLEM. KILLING'S NEVER DONE.
THAT'S WHY WE'RE HERE.
GRAAAGH!
AAAA!

NAH, THIS IS WHY YOU'RE HERE.
YOU'RE GONNA LEARN HOW TO FIGHT. YOU'RE GOOD WITH YOUR ILLUSIONS, BUT COUNTIN' ON 'EM TOO MUCH IS GONNA GET YOU DEAD.
EVEN WHEN THEY FEEL SO REAL THEY WORK ON PEOPLE WHO KNOW THEY'RE FAKE?
YOU JUST THREW YOURSELF BACKWARD AS HARD AS YOU COULD, 'CAUSE IT FELT LIKE YOU SHOULD.
SEEMS TO ME YOU'RE THE ONE WHO NEEDS TRAINING.
THAT'S ENOUGH. YOU COULDA HURT HER.
HEH...HURT HER? I'D SWEAR I WAS ALL TORN UP.
BUT IF YOU WANNA TEACH HER, BE MY GUEST. I GOT PLENTY'A PAIN TO GO AROUND.

THE NEXT DAY
YETI. FINDIN' YOUR BROTHER'S GONNA BE TOUGH. GETTIN' HIM OUT ALIVE'LL BE **TOUGHER.**
YOU'RE STRONG. YOU AIN' FIGHTER. A IN YOU NATURE
YOU BEEN GETTING BY ON BRUTE STRENGTH.
OR SCARIN' PEOPLE AWAY SO YOU DON'T **HAVE** TA FIGHT.
AIN'T GONNA WORK NO MORE.
SSSLIKT
MY HAIR! YOU **IDIOT!** DO YOU HAVE ANY IDEA OF THE SIGNIFICANCE LONG HAIR HAS IN MY CULTURE?
DON'T CARE, HIPPIE. IF IT'S IMPORTANT TA YOU...

...FIGHT FOR IT.
GOOD. BUT THE WEAKEST POINT IN MOST BODIES IS THE MIND.
YOU GOTTA KNOW YOUR ENEMY. FIGURE OUT WHAT GNAWS AT HIS HEART...WHAT WAKES HIM UP AT NIGHT SCREAMING... AND SHOVE IT IN HIS FACE.
HEH.
CLEVER TRICK, HOLO... BUT YER STILL TOO EASY TO SNEAK UP ON.
THESE BOILS... THEY'RE THE ENERGY INSIDE YOU, TRYIN' TO GET OUT. AND IT'S GONNA, ONE WAY OR THE OTHER.
THE TRICK IS TO DO IT WHEN YOU WANT.
FOCUS. DRAW IT ALL TO YOUR HANDS.
FEEL IT TAKE SHAPE...
...AND LET IT GO.
BWHOOOOM
ALL RIGHT!
"YOU'LL GET BETTER."

I'VE BEEN LOOKING THROUGH THE DICTIONARY. GOT A CODE NAME ALL PICKED OUT. "BOMBASTIC AGHAST!" IS THAT RIGHTEOUS OR IS THAT RIGHTEOUS?
JUST WHAT YOU WANT IN A FIGHT, A CODE NAME THAT TAKES HALF AN HOUR TO SAY. STICK WITH "BOMB."
BUT YOU'RE COMING ALONG, KID. THINK YOU'RE READY FOR A RECRUITING MISSION?
ARGENTINA.
SEÑOR KRAUSE?
OR SHOULD I SAY HERR KRAUSE?
REPARACION DE AUTOMOUILES
I HAVE A CONFESSION TO MAKE. I HAVE NOT COME FOR THE ENGINE TO A 1955 CORVETTE.
THE KRAUT CAN'T TALK.
WHO--?

WHUP WHUP WHUP
HE HAD AN ACCIDENT.
THINK OF IT AS A SHOW OF FAITH.
AND SHOULD I THANK YOU FOR HUNTING ME?
COME OUT OF THAT VEHICLE OR DIE IN IT.

WHO ARE YOU?
NAME'S LOGAN. THAT'S CREED. WE GOT SOMETHIN' IN COMMON WITH YOU.
BEEN PUTTIN' TOGETHER A SQUAD'A FOLKS LIKE US.
MUTANTS, OU MEAN? AND OU INTEND TO D OTHER FREAKS E OURSELVES SO E MAY JOIN A FREAK SHOW?
HAVE YOU NO SHAME?
IT'S SURVIVAL, SNOW-TOP. BACK HOME, THE FEDS'RE ROUNDIN' "FREAKS" UP.
I AM NOT SURPRISED. A GOVERNMENT THAT ABSOLVES NAZI DEVILS LIKE VON BRAUN AND STRUGHOLD SIMPLY TO EXPLOIT THEIR GENIUS WILL INEVITABLY ADOPT THEIR METHODS.
YEAH, WHATEVER. POINT IS, WE'RE GONNA SHUT 'EM DOWN. AND WE NEED YER HELP.
DON'T BE FOOLS. FOR THAT, YOU NEED A TRAINED ARMY. MONEY. METICULOUS PLANS.
WITHOUT THAT, YOU WILL SPUR THE HUMANS TO EXTERMINATE US ALL THE SOONER.
LET'S GO. GUY'S A WIMP. ONLY UP FOR FIGHTIN' OLD MEN.
YOU WILL GO NOWHERE UNTIL YOU AGREE TO ABANDON YOUR SUICIDAL COURSE!

YOU'RE THE SUICIDAL ONE.
YOU DON'T WANNA HELP, BUB, THAT'S YOUR CALL. YOU TRY TO STOP US WE GOT A PROBLEM.
SNIKT
I AM A MASTER OF MAGNETISM!
YOU'VE CHOSEN YOUR BATTLEFIELD POORLY.
SPHAMM
WHRANKT
AND YOU DONE FORGOT WHERE YOU CAME FROM.
LET'S REFRESH YOUR MEMORY.
HOLO!

OH...GOD...
IN...HEAVEN...
NO...
HALT!
YOUR TIME HAS COME, JUDEN.
N-NO...
NO.
AN... IMPRESSIVE ILLUSION.
HE'S SHAKIN' IT OFF!
BRUKK
BUT ONLY ONE WHO HAS BEEN TO THE CAMPS KNOWS THEIR TRUE HORROR.
A CHILD WHO HAS ONLY SEEN IT ON TELEVISION DOES NOT.
UHH!

YOU WANT HORROR? I GOT SOME RIGHT HERE.
GNNH!
BWHOOM
YOU ARE... POWERFUL, CHILDREN.
THRAMM
BUT YOU ARE STILL CHILDREN.

HOLY...

ARE YOU TRULY PREPARED TO REAP WHAT YOU SOW?
ARE YOU READY FOR WAR?
"READY?"
MY WHOLE DAMN LIFE IS WAR!
NNAAHH!
TAXI

THESE KIDS ARE GONNA HAVE BETTER. THEY WON'T BE ANYBODY'S LAB RAT OR WEAPON.
YOU THINK WE AIN'T AFRAID TO KILL FOR THAT? YOU THINK WE AIN'T AFRAID TO DIE?
HOW ABOUT YOU, BIG MAN? ARE YOU AFRAID TO DIE?
I AM NOT.
BUT I WILL NOT SLAUGHTER MY OWN KIND. THERE ARE TOO FEW OF US. EVERY LIFE IS PRECIOUS.
KINDA MY THINKIN'.
THEN I WILL HOPE YOU COME TO YOUR SENSES.
AND IF YOU DO NOT...WHEN YOUR MADNESS LEADS TO YOUR DOOM...
...I WILL RAISE A GLASS TO YOUR MEMORY.
GET BACK HERE AND FIGHT LIKE A MAN, YOU SON OF A--
LEAVE IT. HE'S RIGHT. WE AIN'T DOIN' THIS TO KILL EACH OTHER.
AND WE GOT BIGGER PROBLEMS THAN HIM.

N
DISCLOSED
CATION!
FLYING MURDERE
STRIKES IN ARGENTIN
NAZI SUPERM
IN HIDIN
FORCED TO SHUT DOWN OUR OWN RESEARCH CENTER! TO RUN LIKE RABBITS! NOW REPORTS OF MURDER AND MASS DESTRUCTION IN ARGENTINA!
WHAT HAVE I BEEN SAYING? IT WAS ONLY A MATTER OF TIME UNTIL THESE... CREATURES STARTED ORGANIZING. WHILE WE HOLD MEETINGS, THEY'RE FORMING ARMIES!
AND YOU WANT TO SPEND BILLIONS ON ROBOTS TO HUNT THEM WITH. WE ALL KNOW HOW YOU FEEL ABOUT THIS, BOLIVAR.
YOU MAKE IT SOUND LIKE SCIENCE FICTION, DUNCAN. I'M TALKING ABOUT ARTIFICIAL INTELLIGENCE. SOLDIERS WHO CAN ADAPT TO ANYTHING.
WHAT'S YOUR SOLUTION? OFFER THEM DENTAL BENEFITS TO COME WORK FOR US? THEY'RE MONSTERS!
SOME, SURE. OTHERS ARE LOYAL AMERICANS, WITH TALENTS WE CAN USE.
LOYAL--? THEY'RE NOT HUMAN, FRED! DO YOU FEEL LOYALTY TO APES?
THAT'S ENOUGH, GENTLEMEN. YOU'RE HERE BECAUSE WE VALUE BOTH YOUR OPINIONS.
DR. TRASK, WE'RE ADDING ANOTHER BILLION FOR YOUR PROJECT: SENTINEL.
BUT THE DIRECTOR SEES MERIT IN AGENT DUNCAN'S APPROACH AS WELL.
WE'VE HAD A HISTORY OF SUCCESS WITH... SPECIAL INDIVIDUALS, GOING BACK TO CAPTAIN AMERICA. PROPERLY SUPERVISED, MEN LIKE LOGAN AND CREED COULD BE ASSETS.
THE PROBLEM HAS ALWAYS BEEN HOW TO CONTROL THEM. WE THINK WE MAY HAVE A SOLUTION.

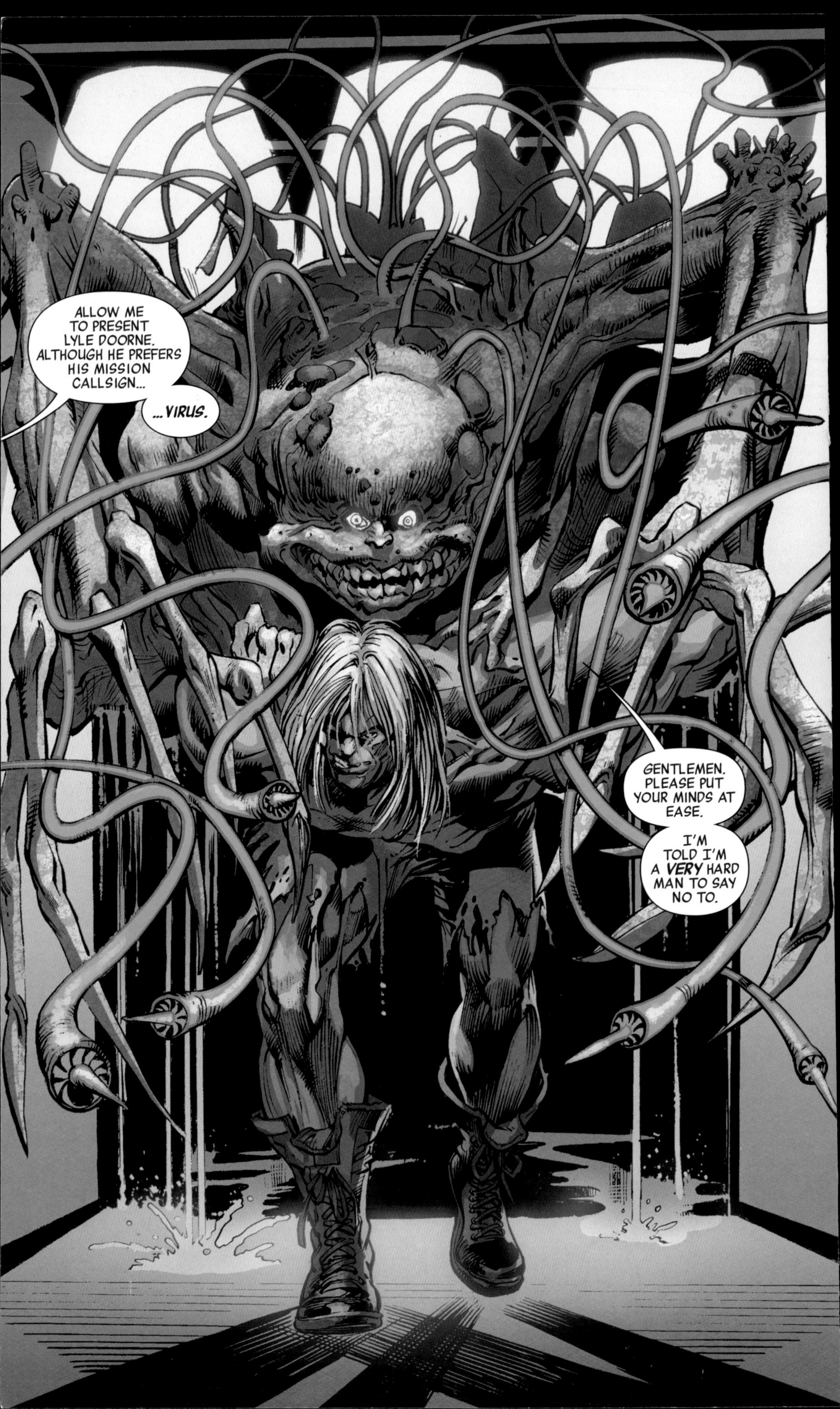
ALLOW ME TO PRESENT LYLE DOORNE. ALTHOUGH HE PREFERS HIS MISSION CALLSIGN...
...VIRUS.
GENTLEMEN. PLEASE PUT YOUR MINDS AT EASE.
I'M TOLD I'M A VERY HARD MAN TO SAY NO TO.

MANHATTAN.
TAKE IT EASY! WE'RE NOT WITH THE MEN WHO ATTACKED YOU!
WE'RE LIKE YOU, YA IDJIT!
NO ONE IS LIKE ME!

=WHUFF!=

GREAT PLAN, LOGAN. A CRAZY SUPER-STRONG HOBO IS EXACTLY WHAT WE NEED ON THIS TEAM.
THE FEDS WENT AFTER HIM, LIKE THEY WENT AFTER YOU. WE COULDN'T JUST LET 'EM TAKE HIM.
OH, GOD, VIC!
LOGAN, HIS BONES... THEY'RE ALL... TWISTED...
CREED'LL HEAL. WATCH YER OWN--
IMPERIUS REX!
LOGAN, LOOK OUT!

BAM
NOT SURE WHAT THAT MEANT, BUT I DON'T WANT TO HURT YOU, BROTHER-- GGH!
NONE OF YOU CAN HURT ME!
FRED THE FED. ONE A' THE GUYS WHO'VE BEEN HUNTIN' AND KIDNAPPIN' PEOPLE LIKE US.
NO. THE ONE WHO'S BEEN TRYING TO CONVINCE THE BUREAU WE SHOULD BE ALLIES, NOT ENEMIES.
CAR WASH
I KNOW YOU DON'T TRUST ME. BUT OUR INTEL SAYS FIRE CAN HURT THIS GUY.
HE TOOK OUT OUR FLAMETHROWER UNITS. YOUR FRIEND WITH THE EXPLOSIVES IS OUR BEST SHOT.
BOMB!
LET'S HAVE A FIREBALL, KID.
BUT YOU'RE IN THE WAY!
WON'T BE THE FIRST TIME. JUST DO IT!

YOU'VE DONE THIS TO ME! LIKE SNAKES IN MY HEAD--CAN'T THINK--
GHAAGH!
BOMB! NOW!
KRNCH

BWHOOOOM
SPLOOSH
HE OKAY, YETI?
FINE. HEY, BOSS, WHERE'S THE OTHER GUY?
NO TRACE OF HIM...RIVER'S LIKE A SEWER. PROBABLY DIDN'T MAKE IT.
DAMN SHAME. GUY WAS HURTIN'. BUT WE COULDN'T LET HIM KILL HALF THE CITY. BESIDES...

...WE GOT
ORE IMMEDIATE
CONCERNS.
STAND DOWN, MEN!
BUT SIR, THE MUTANTS--
THE MUTANTS SAVED YOUR ASS, MAHONEY, AND HUNDREDS OF CIVILIANS. NOW STAND DOWN!
"MUTANTS"? THAT'S WHAT YOU'RE CALLIN' US? REAL CLASSY, DUNCAN.
BUT I'LL GIVE YOU THIS... YOU'RE NOT THE TOTAL JERKWEED I THOUGHT YOU WERE.
HOLO, GIVE US SOME COVER. JUST IN CASE THE REST OF HIS GUYS ARE.
MR. TRASK'S NOT GONNA LIKE THIS, SIR.
DO I LOOK LIKE I CARE?
WHAT ABOUT OUR TARGET? THE ONE WE CAME FOR?
IT'S BEEN
VE MINUTES.
'S DONE FOR,
MAHONEY.
UNLESS HE CAN BREATHE WATER.
WATER...SO FAMILIAR.
I CAN ALMOST REMEMBER...MY HEAD...NEED TO CLEAR MY HEAD, I NEED...
...I NEED A DRINK...

LOGAN'S CABIN, UPSTATE.
VIC? YOU OKAY?
DOWNSIDE OF HAVING A HEALING FACTOR... THE BONES SET WRONG. I GOTTA RE-BREAK 'EM.
GET ON BACK TO THE CABIN, HOLLY. YOU DON'T WANNA SEE THIS.
NO, I'D RATHER...
NNAAGGHH!
KRA
OH MY GOD!
YOU SHOULD TAKE OFF, KID.
I... I COULD MAKE AN ILLUSION, TO TAKE YOUR MIND OFF IT. A HAPPY MEMORY.
I HAD ANY, I'D TAKE YOU UP ON THAT.
THERE ISN'T ANYTHING I CAN DO?
JUST... TELL ME ABOUT YOURSELF. WHERE YOU'RE FROM, LIKE THAT.
O-OKAY...
I WAS BORN IN HAVRE DE GRACE, MARYLAND. MY MOM LEFT WHEN I WAS FIVE. WELL, MY DAD SAID SHE LEFT. HE WAS... KIND OF A SCARY GUY.
YOU REMEMBER HER?
LITTLE THINGS. THE WA SHE SMELLED... A NECKLACE...
KRAK

GGGGRRHRR!
RIKK
OH, VIC...
K-KEEP TALKIN'.
W-WHEN I WAS ELEVEN, I STARTED MAKING IMAGES OF MY MOM. SHE'D TAKE CARE OF ME...TELL ME SHE LOVED ME. ONE DAY MY DAD SAW.
HE STARTED CHARGING PEOPLE TO COME OVER, AND HAVE ME CREATE WHATEVER FANTASY THEY WANTED. A LOT WERE...BAD.

CUM...I'LL ILL 'IM...
TOO LATE. HE OVERDOSED WHEN I WAS FIFTEEN.

I'VE BEEN ON MY OWN EVER SINCE.

UNTIL NOW.

YOU REALLY THINK THAT FED'S GONNA SQUARE THINGS FOR US?
"SQUARE" THINGS? THEY KIDNAPPED MY BROTHER! HOW DO YOU "SQUARE" THAT?
YETI'S RIGHT. EVEN IF DUNCAN'S A STAND-UP GUY, HE'S JUST A COG IN THE MACHINE.
BUT IF HE'S THINKIN' ABOUT A CHANGE'A COURSE, IT MEANS WHAT WE'RE DOING IS WORKING.
I KNOW HOW THES BUREAUCRATS OPER IT'S ALL ABOUT BUD WE GOTTA MAKE IT HURTIN' US--HUNT "MUTANTS"--IS TO EXPENSIVE.
WE ALREADY SHUT DOWN ON BASE. COST 'EM LOT OF MONEY. T TO DO IT AGAIN. YE WE'RE GOIN' AFT YER BROTHER.
ABOUT TIME.
I FINALLY GOT A LEAD ON WHERE THEY MIGHT BE KEEPIN' HIM. WE GOT LUCKY--DUNCAN LEFT NEW YORK IN A CAR INSTEAD OF A PLANE. I TRACKED HIM TO PENNSYLVANIA.
I WANT YO BOTH MISSIC READY BY SU AND YETI-- NEED YOUR HEAD IN TH GAME.
HEY!
WHAT THE HELL ARE YOU DOING?
SHOWING MORE'A YOUR FACE. WHICH IS NOT AN IMPROVEMENT.
I WAS MAKING A POINT.
YOU LET YOURSELF GET DISTRACTED, YOU'RE KILLIN' YOUR BROTHER. AND US. REMEMBER THAT.
CREED. WE GOT SOME PLANNING TO DO.
CREED! WHAT THE HELL'RE YOU DOIN' IN THERE?
NONE A' YOUR BUSINESS.
CUT THE CRAP. I CAN SMELL HER.
NOW COME OUT BEFORE I BREAK THE DAMN DOOR DOWN.

I'D ASK IF U'RE CRAZY IF I T ALREADY KNOW. T EVEN FOR YOU, HIS IS CROSSIN' A LINE.
"JAILBAIT," YOU CALLED HER THE NIGHT WE MET.
SHE'S EIGHTEEN. OLD ENOUGH TO MAKE HER OWN DECISIONS, WHETHER YOU LIKE 'EM OR NOT.
IT AIN'T JUST THE AGE. WE'RE THEIR SQUAD LEADERS. WE GIVE THESE KIDS ORDERS...TAKE 'EM INTO COMBAT.
IF THAT'S A PROBLEM, LEMME SOLVE IT.
I QUIT. I'M TAKIN' HOLLY AND LEAVING. WE GOT TOO MUCH HEAT ON US, LOGAN.
THAT HEAT'S 'CAUSE WE'RE WINNING. WE GOT A CHANCE TO DO SOMETHING BIG HERE!
SO DO I!
YOU KNOW THE LAST TIME I THOUGHT ABOUT SETTLING DOWN? HAVIN' A REAL LIFE? NEVER!
I ACCEPTED A LONG TIME AGO THAT I WAS A MONSTER, AN' I WAS ALWAYS GONNA BE A MONSTER. HELL, I GOT TO LIKE IT.
I DIDN'T MIND TAKIN' ON THE U.S. GOVERNMENT. WE DIE, SO WHAT? NO BIG LOSS. BUT NOW...
I GOT A SHOT HERE, LOGAN. A SHOT AT SOMETHING BETTER.
U FEEL IT TOO, DON'T YA? THE AIR ON THE BACK OF YER NECK STANDIN' UP. THE INSTINCT TO GO TO GROUND.
THAT... THAT'S ALL IT IS. THE INSTINCT OF ANIMALS AIN'T USED TO STAYIN' IN ONCE PLACE TOO LONG.
GUYS? CAN I SAY SOMETHING?

VIC...I KNOW WHAT YOU'RE FEELING. FOR THE FIRST TIME IN OUR LIVES, WE'VE GOT A HOME...
...A PLACE TO BELONG. I WANT TO GIVE THAT TO OTHERS. PEOPLE LIKE US...MUTANTS... WHO'VE NEVER HAD IT.
YEAH. WE GOT THE BEST CHANCE WE'RE EVER GONNA HAVE. FOR US AND EVERYONE LIKE US. BUT ONLY IF WE STAND AND FIGHT.
WE BACK DOWN NOW, THEY'LL SMELL WEAKNESS. AND THEY'LL NEVER LEAVE US ALONE.
THEN I'M STAYING.
HOW ABOUT YOU?
I...
FINE.
BUT YOU BETTER BE RIGHT ABOUT THIS, LOGAN.
YOU JUST DAMN WELL BETTER BE RIGHT.

E PENTAGON.
ITHORITIES INSIST THE MAGE WAS CAUSED BY GAS MAIN EXPLOSION, COUNTING REPORTS OF N INCREDIBLY STRONG AN AS THE FANTASIES OF UNRELIABLE OR EBRIATED WITNESSES.
WE ASKED MANHATTAN'S ASSISTANT DIRECTOR OF THE F.B.I. ABOUT THE ECENT RASH OF SIGHTINGS OF BEINGS WITH SUPERNATURAL POWERS. HE HAD THIS TO SAY:
IT'S LIKE UFOS. WE LIVE IN PARANOID TIMES. IF PEOPLE ARE SCARED, WE'RE GLAD TO INVESTIGATE.
USUALLY THAT'S THE END OF IT... THESE BOOGEYMEN ARE NEVER SEEN AGAIN.
PRIVATE XAVIER. COME IN.
YOU'LL HAVE FORGIVE ME, CAN'T RECALL E REASON FOR IS MEETING...
TO DISCUSS MY FILE.
Y-YES. IT'S CLEAR. ANYONE WITH YOUR LEVEL OF I.Q. GETS FLAGGED--
--BUT WHEN YOU ENLISTED, YOUR BLOOD TESTED AS NORMAL HUMAN.
OF COURSE... IT WAS THE DOCTOR'S BLOOD. NOW LET ME GET BACK TO MY FIANCÉE BEFORE SHE LEAVES ME.
WH--EXCUSE ME, I... GOT DISTRACTED. GIVEN THE TRAGIC LOSS OF YOUR BROTHER, WE CAN OFFER YOU COMPASSIONATE LEAVE...
...OR EVEN DISCHARGE.
memo: THE UTANT ENACE
from: BOLIVAR TRASK
OF COURSE, A YOUNG MAN WITH A PROMISING CAREER MIGHT PREFER ANOTHER ASSIGNMENT. STATESIDE. ONE WITH GREAT RESPONSIBILITY.
A FRIEND OF MINE IS IN CHARGE OF A SPECIAL, TOP-SECRET F.B.I. PROJECT...
THANK YOU, COLONEL. THAT DOES SOUND LIKE IT COULD BE MOST... INTRIGUING.
MAKE IT SO.

PENNSYLVANIA. PROJECT CHIMERA HEADQUARTERS. CLASSIFICATION: SECRET.
YOU'RE A MUTANT!
OH, COME ON, TRASK! WE'VE ALL BEEN GENETICALLY SCREENED.
Federal Bureau of Investigation
THEN YOU'RE INCOMPETENT...OR WORSE, A TRAITOR TO YOUR RACE!
YOU HAD LOGAN AND HIS MONSTERS DEAD TO RIGHTS, AND YOU LET THEM GO?
WHAT I HAD WAS A STANDOFF WITH FIVE MUTANTS AT FULL POWER, AGAINST A STRIKE TEAM THAT'D BEEN BEATEN TO A PULP BY THE TARGET YOU SENT US AFTER OVER MY OBJECTIONS.
AND WITH MINIMAL INTEL ASIDE FROM VAGUE RUMORS OF A SUPER-STRONG HOMELESS MAN. YOU'RE THE DANGEROUS ONE.
I WILL NOT STAND HERE AND BE SECOND-GUESSED BY SOMEONE WHO'S NEVER BEEN IN THE FIELD!
THAT'S ENOUGH. DUNCAN, YOU REALLY THINK YOU CAN GET LOGAN AND HIS PEOPLE TO WORK FOR US WILLINGLY?
THEY DON'T TR
WHO CARES?
LOGAN AND CREED ARE LOOSE CANNONS. THEY MUST BE TREATED LIKE VOLATILE EXPLOSIVES, NOT REASONABLE MEN.
GOOD LORD.
BUT NOT TO WORRY, MR. HARTFIELD. I WILL SOLVE ALL YOUR PROBLEMS.
NEUTRALIZE THE THREAT WHILE ADDING THEIR POWER TO YOUR RANKS...IN CONTROLLED FORM.

OF COURSE, I'LL NEED A NEW MOUNT. I'M AFRAID THIS ONE'S RUNNING ON FUMES.
I THINK YOU'LL BE HAPPY WITH WHAT WE'VE BROUGHT YOU. GENTLEMEN, PLEASE BRING IN THE PRISONER.
M-MR. HARTFIELD? YOU SAID I COULD SEE MY BROTHER...
AND YOU WILL, FORREST. VERY SOON. BUT I'D LIKE YOU TO MEET SOMEONE ELSE NOW. HE'S CALLED **VIRUS.**
AH, YES. STRONG AND HARDY. THIS ONE WILL DO VERY NICELY.
WHAT DOES THAT MEAN?
IT MEANS I KNOW I LOOK ODD, BUT THAT'S BECAUSE I'M LIKE YOU...A MUTANT. AND I WANT US TO BE THE CLOSEST OF FRIENDS. WOULDN'T YOU LIKE THAT?
I-I GUESS...
GOOD.
BECAUSE, REALLY, YOU DON'T HAVE A CHOICE.
AGENT DUNCAN, THERE'S BEEN A PERIMETER BREACH.

AAAGGH!
MY BROTHER... IN PAIN...
YOU BETTER SHUT UP OR WE'RE ALL GONNA BE IN--
AOOGA AOOGA
AHH, CRAP.
OKAY...
...LET'S DO THIS.
RRRAAAGGHH!

WHAT--OUR MEN ARE FIGHTING EMPTY AIR!
THE GIRL. IN THE FILES LOGAN AND CREED STOLE, THERE WAS A GIRL WHO CREATES INCREDIBLY VIVID ILLUSIONS--
SMART FELLA.
NOT SMART ENOUGH.
LOGAN, ATTACKING US STUPID. YOU'RE HURTING OURSELF. WE CAN WORK SOMETHING OUT--
NOT WHILE YOU'RE HOLDIN' OUR PEOPLE. WE CAN TALK AFTER YOU LET 'EM OUT. STARTIN' WITH MY FRIEND'S BROTHER.
ASK AND YE SHALL RECEIVE.
YOU SHOULD CONSIDER JOINING US. I, FOR ONE, LOVE MY JOB.
OH, NO...

FORREST, WHAT DID THEY DO TO YOU?
MADE HIM USEFUL. DON'T WORRY, I'LL DO THE SAME FOR YOU.
TRAITOR. YOU'RE LIKE US, AND YOU WORK FOR THEM?
BOMB, NO! DON'T HURT HIM!
HE AIN'T MY BROTHER. YOU ARE.
AND IF HE'S AS TOUGH AS YOU, HE'LL BE FINE.
THE FREAK RIDING HIM, THOUGH--
WHOOM
THERE'S YOUR ANSWER. EVEN TO MY OWN KIND, I'M A "FREAK."
WHOA!
I'M NOT LIKE YOU. MY MUTATION DIDN'T MAKE ME HANDSOME OR STRONG. JUST BETTER ABLE TO SURVIVE.
YEAH?

LET'S TEST THAT.
SHHLKT
GNNAAAHH!
YETI, GET'CHER BROTHER. C'MON, THEY GOT OTHER PRISONERS. THE CELLS ARE THIS WAY.
WANT ME TO KILL THE LEECH?
NO TIME. LEAVE HIM, HE DON'T MATTER NOW. BESIDES...
WHO KNOWS WHAT YOU COULD CATCH TOUCHIN' A SLUG WHO LOOKS LIKE THAT?
WE STICK TO THE MISSION. WE'RE HERE TO FREE THE PRISONERS.
AND HOPEFULLY GET OURSELVES SOME NEW RECRUITS.

LOOKIT THESE YAHOOS. SO MUCH FOR RECRUITS.
THEY LOOK LIKE THEY'LL BE DEAD WEIGHT IN A FIGHT.
RIGHT BACK ATCHA, OLD MAN.
WE'RE BUSTIN' OUT. C'MON IF YOU WANT, BUT YOU SENIOR CITIZENS BETTER KEEP UP.
HEY, KIDDO. HOW YOU DOIN'?
OH, FINE. MY BRAIN FEELS LIKE IT'S GOING TO BURST OUT OF MY HEAD, THAT'S ALL. I CAN'T KEEP THIS UP MUCH LONGER.
YOU DONE PLENTY.
NO NEED FOR ILLUSIO ANYMORE.
I'M TAKIN' YOU HOME.
BWHOOOM
WE'RE ALL GOI HOME.

ALL RIGHT. I AIN'T ONE TO TOSS AROUND COMPLIMENTS, BUT YOU KIDS DID GOOD TONIGHT.
WE GOT OUR PEOPLE OUT. WE MADE THE FEDS PAY FOR TAKIN' 'EM. WE SHOWED 'EM WE'RE NOT GONNA ROLL OVER.
AND WE SHOWED 'EM WE STAND TOGETHER.
WE GOTTA PLAN FOR RETALIATION. BUT IF THEY'RE SMART, THEY'LL START TALKING ABOUT A DEAL.
WE JUST GAVE OURSELVES THE BEST CHANCE WE'RE EVER GONNA HAVE FOR A FUTURE.
IF WE PLAY OUR CARDS RIGHT...
"...WE'LL LOOK BACK ON THIS AS THE DAY THINGS TURNED AROUND."
THE SEED HAS BEEN PLANTED. SOON THEY WILL BE YOURS...
OURS...

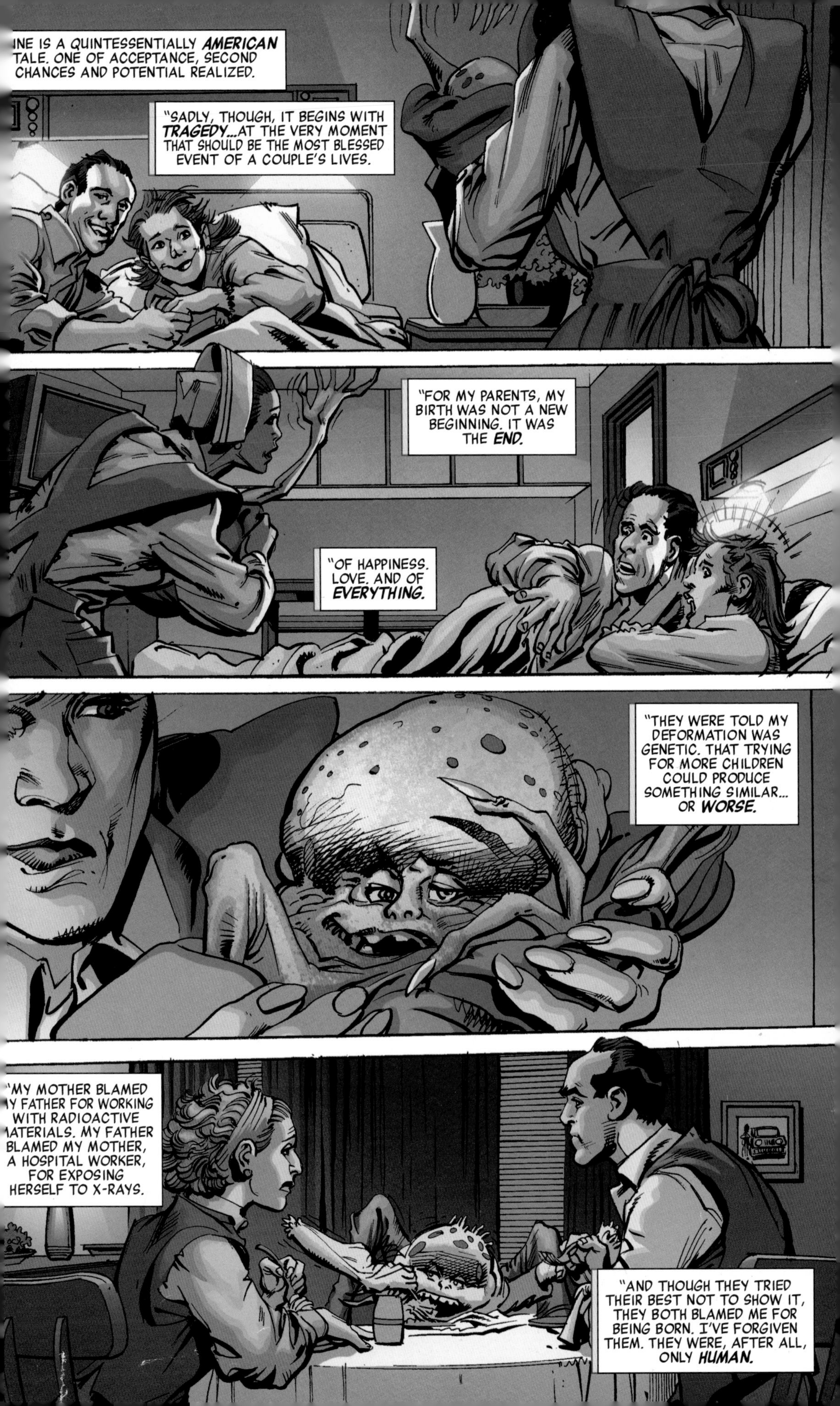
INE IS A QUINTESSENTIALLY AMERICAN TALE. ONE OF ACCEPTANCE, SECOND CHANCES AND POTENTIAL REALIZED.
"SADLY, THOUGH, IT BEGINS WITH TRAGEDY...AT THE VERY MOMENT THAT SHOULD BE THE MOST BLESSED EVENT OF A COUPLE'S LIVES.
"FOR MY PARENTS, MY BIRTH WAS NOT A NEW BEGINNING. IT WAS THE END.
"OF HAPPINESS. LOVE. AND OF EVERYTHING.
"THEY WERE TOLD MY DEFORMATION WAS GENETIC. THAT TRYING FOR MORE CHILDREN COULD PRODUCE SOMETHING SIMILAR... OR WORSE.
"MY MOTHER BLAMED Y FATHER FOR WORKING WITH RADIOACTIVE ATERIALS. MY FATHER BLAMED MY MOTHER, A HOSPITAL WORKER, FOR EXPOSING HERSELF TO X-RAYS.
"AND THOUGH THEY TRIED THEIR BEST NOT TO SHOW IT, THEY BOTH BLAMED ME FOR BEING BORN. I'VE FORGIVEN THEM. THEY WERE, AFTER ALL, ONLY HUMAN.

"THEY KEPT ME IN THE ATTIC. TO PROTECT ME, I'M CERTAIN, FROM A CRUEL AND PREJUDICED WORLD. I DIDN'T MIND.
"I HAD FRIENDS. THE MICE WOULD DO TRICKS FOR ME...
"...UNTIL THEY DIED.
"ONE DAY, MOTHER CHANGED. SHE BROUGHT ME OUT OF THE ATTIC AND SHOWERED ME WITH LOVE.
SPORTS
BUGLE
"THEN SHE DIED, TOO. A VIRUS, THEY SAID.

"MY FATHER KNEW WHO WAS RESPONSIBLE. HE SAID I HAD A SICKNESS IN ME. THAT I WAS EVIL.
"I WAS A CHILD. ALL I WANTED WAS THE LOVE OF MY MOTHER...

"...AND MY FATHER FOR THEM TO ACCEPT ME...

"...AND SUPPORT ME, AS A PARENT SHOULD.
"I LOST EVERYTHING THAT DAY. MY HOME, MY FATHER...THE ONLY WORLD I'D EVER KNOWN.

"IT WAS SO VERY VERY SAD.
"IT WAS THE WORST MOMENT OF MY LIFE."

HOW DID YOU COME TO...SERVE YOUR COUNTRY, LYLE?
"VIRUS," PLEASE, AGENT DUNCAN. AND THAT, I AM GRATIFIED TO SAY, IS WHERE MY STORY TAKES A HAPPY TURN.
"MY FATHER WORKED IN A GOVERNMENT FACILITY. WEAPONS RESEARCH. I SAW IN HIS MIND THAT THEY WERE FORWARD-THINKING, HIGH-MINDED MEN.
"THEY SAW THE POTENTIAL OF MY GIFTS. REALIZED I COULD USE THEM FOR THE MUTUAL BENEFIT OF MYSELF AND MY NATION.
"I'M LIKE YOU AND AGENT DANSIG. I BELIEVE HUMANITY CAN WORK TOGETHER WITH...'MUTANTS,' I THINK YOU CALL US."
HAT MEN OF VISION IN BOTH OUR SPECIES HAVE A DUTY TO REIN IN THE EXCESSES OF THE LESS ENLIGHTENED.
MR. LOGAN AND HIS FRIENDS BELIEVE THEY'VE WON A GREAT VICTORY. LIBERATED THEIR FELLOWS. AUGMENTED THEIR RIDICULOUS REVOLUTIONARY ARMY.
"THEY HAVE NO IDEA I AM AMONG THEM. OR RATHER, MY MOUNT. IT WILL BE SIMPLE TO BRING THEM UNDER OUR CONTROL."
YOU CAN RECRUIT THE MORE REASONABLE ONES. AND LEAVE THE REST TO ME.
WELL, MAKE IT FAST. BECAUSE THERE ARE OTHER IDEAS. LIKE TRASK'S PROJECT SENTINEL.
AND TEMPERS ARE GETTING HOT ALL AROUND.

LOGAN'S CABIN, UPSTATE.
MR. LOGAN'S THE BOSS. HE SAVED US. WE DO WHAT HE SAYS!
I WAS IN THE ARMY. I KNOW HOW THESE GUYS THINK. THEY'LL NEVER STOP COMING. WE EITHER HIT THEM NOW OR DIE.
IF YOU'RE SO SMART, WHY DIDN'T YOU HELP US ESCAPE?
THAT'S IT, FEEB. I'M GONNA KICK YOUR--
NO.
HEY, I GOT--
AW, YER KIDDING ME.
ANOTHER FIGHT?
YOU COME AT MY BROTHER, YOU COME AT ME.
FINE BY ME HAIRBALL!

OCK OFF.
BACK UP, METEOR.
GO TO HELL! I DON'T REMEMBER YOU WINNING ANY DAMN ELECTION!
YOU WANNA CALL THE SHOTS, PROVE YOU'RE BETTER QUALIFIED THAN ME!
HRRGH!
THAT'S ENOUGH.
SPTT--
I JUST SAVED YOUR LIFE, METEOR. YOU CAN THANK ME LATER.
THAT HOSE ISN'T EVEN REAL, HOLO. IT'S ONE OF YOUR ILLUSIONS.
BUT THE WATER FEELS REAL, DOESN'T IT? REAL ENOUGH THAT YOUR MIND WON'T LET YOU BLAZE UP AGAIN.
SOMEBODY TELL ME WHAT THIS BRAWL'S ABOUT BEFORE I JUST KICK EVERYONE'S ASS.

METEOR STARTED IT, MR. LOGAN.
YOU'RE SUCH A BROWN-NOSER, BOMB.
STOP. WE GOT TOO MANY ENEMIES TO BE FIGHTIN' EACH OTHER.
YOU WANNA BLOW OFF STEAM, FINE. METEOR. YETI. TEN MILE RUN.
UNLESS ONE'A YOU WANTS TA PROV YOU SHOULD BE RUNN THE SHOW.
NOT TODAY.
BUT IF YOU DON'T START ACTING LIKE A LEADER... SOON.
HE'S WRONG, ISN'T HE? THEY'RE NOT GOING TO COME AFTER US, ARE THEY?
I DON'T WANT TO GO BACK TO THAT PLACE. DON'T LET THEM TAKE ME, MR. LOGAN...
THEY WON'T, FORREST. COME ON. LET'S PLAY MONOPOLY.
OKAY, HOLO.
I LIKE PLAYING GAMES.

NOW THAT THAT'S OVER... BOMB, I GOT YA SOMETHING.
FOR ME? REALLY?
IT'S YOUR SIZE. WON'T GET IN YOUR WAY IN A FIGHT.
I DIDN'T ASK FOR A DAMN COAT. YOU ALREADY GAVE ME A DAMN COAT. SUITS ME JUST FINE.
BWHOOM
YOU KEEP WASTIN' YOUR TIME ON NONSENSE LIKE THAT, MAYBE METEOR'S RIGHT ABOUT YOU.
THE HELL WAS THAT ABOUT?
DAMN, LOGAN, I THOUGHT I WAS THICK. YOU'RE DOWNRIGHT STUPID.
ANYWAY, THAT METEOR KID MAY BE A PUNK...BUT HE'S GOT A POINT.
YOU WERE ALL ABOUT PUTTIN' TOGETHER AN ARMY. WELL, YOU GOT ONE, AND THEY'RE GETTIN' RESTLESS... EVEN THE PRESIDENT'A YOUR FAN CLUB. IT'S TIME TO FISH OR CUT BAIT.

DON'T YOU START. THEY'RE STILL TOO RAW. WE'LL MOVE WHEN THEY'RE READY.
AND DO WHAT? FILL A MORGUE WITH FEDS? THEY'LL NEVER GET OFF OUR BACKS.
LIKE I SAID, IT'S ABOUT MONEY. WE WRECK THEIR BASES... EQUIPMENT. MAKE COMIN' AFTER US EXPENSIVE.
THEN MAYBE THEY'LL LISTEN TO DUNCAN AND CUT US A DEAL.
DEAL? WHAT KINDA DEAL?
YOU'RE NOT STUPID, CREED. YOU KNOW THE KINDA JOBS GOVERNMENTS FIND FOR GUYS LIKE US.
SOME FOLKS ARE SUITED TO IT. YOU. ME. PROBABLY METEOR. SOME AIN'T.
THIS IS ABOUT PROTECTING THEM. GIVIN' 'EM A CHOICE.
THE FEDS WANT WHAT WE GOT TA OFFER, THEY LEAVE THE OTHERS ALONE.
SO WHAT YOU'RE SAYIN' IS NOTHING CHANGES.
FOR US? TOO LATE FOR US.
IT AIN'T TOO LATE FOR THEM.

THEY DESERVE A SHOT AT A NORMAL LIFE. THEY'RE YOUNG. HAVEN'T SEEN WHAT WE'VE SEEN.
CREED... YOU MENTIONED
MAYBE YOU SHOULD.
SHE WOULDN'T GO. AND I AIN'T SURE I WOULD EITHER, NOW.
FROM THE DAY I WAS BORN, EVERYONE'S BEEN TELLIN' ME I'M A MONSTER. GUESS IN A LOTTA WAYS I AM. PROBABLY ALWAYS WILL BE.
BUT THIS... YOU WERE RIGHT, LOGAN. THIS IS OUR CHANCE TO BE SOMETHING **BETTER.** SOMETHING **REAL.**
WE'LL MAKE IT WORK.
OR DIE TRYIN'.

EVERYBODY CALMED DOWN?
CALM AS THEY GET.
CREED'S RIGHT. WE GOTTA MAKE OUR MOVE. TOMORROW, WE GO ON THE OFFENSIVE.
HE REALLY LOVES YOU, YA KNOW.
YEAH. I KNOW.
THAT'S IT? "I KNOW?"
WHAT DO YOU WANT ME TO SAY? I'M **EIGHTEEN.** I CARE ABOUT HIM...A LOT. BUT I DON'T KNOW **WHAT** I WANT TO DO WITH THE REST OF MY LIFE.
ALL I KNOW IS, FOR THE FIRST TIME, I FEEL LIKE I MIGHT HAVE A CHOICE.
VIC, TOO. I HAVEN'T KNOWN HIM AS LONG AS YOU, BUT I CAN SEE HOW HE'S CHANGED. I KNOW PART OF THAT'S ME, BUT PART OF IT'S WHAT WE'RE DOING.
I WISH THAT BALD KID HAD JOINED US...XAVIER. LEHNSHERR, THE MAGNE GUY. THEY HAD THAT. ***THING.*** THAT ***LEADER*** HAVE.
I GOT WHAT ***GRUNTS*** HAVE. I'LL KILL WHAT YA POINT AT, AND IF THEY PUT DOWN, I'LL KEEP GETT UP 'TIL I CAN'T GET UP NO MORE.
THAT AIN'T A LEADER.
YOU'RE WRONG. YOU BROUGHT US TOGETHER. TRAINED US. GAVE US A PURPOSE. IF THAT'S NOT A LEADER, I DON'T KNOW WHAT IS.
WE BELIEVE IN YOU. WE'LL FOLLOW YOU. MAYBE THINGS'LL WORK OUT, MAYBE THEY WON'T.
BUT WE HAVE A ***CHANCE.*** SOMETHING WE NEVER HAD BEFORE.
THAT'S BECAUSE OF ***YOU.***

WHAT THE HELL--WE'RE MOBILIZING?
WHERE'S HARTFIELD? ON WHOSE AUTHORITY IS THIS HAPPENING?
MINE. THEY'RE PLANNING TO STRIKE AT US BEFORE DAWN. I SAW IT.
MR. HARTFIELD, IF YOU GIVE ME A CHANCE, I CAN WORK SOMETHING OUT WITH THEM--
THE TIME FOR NEGOTIATION IS OVER, AGENT DUNCAN. IF YOU THINK YOU CAN TALK THEM INTO SURRENDERING, COME ON. BUT BE ADVISED...
...WE'RE TRYING TRASK'S APPROACH, TOO. THE SENTINELS ARE A GO.
GOD...
YOU. PRIVATE...
XAVIER, SIR.
YEAH, WHATEVER. GOT ROOM IN THAT VEHICLE FOR ME?
IT HAPPENS I DO, SIR.

OKAY, THIS IS FOR REAL. I WANT EVERYONE ORGANIZED AND DISCIPLINED. DO YOUR JOB, KEEP AN EYE ON YOUR PARTNERS AND WE'LL BE--
LOGAN!
YOU BACKSTABBING PIECE'A--YOU CAN'T STAND IT, CAN YOU? HAVIN' SOMETHING YOU DON'T?
SURE WE ARE.
KRAK
YOU'D KNOW HIM BETTER'N ME, YETI. BUT HE SEEMS KINDA OFF, DON'T HE?
THE SPOOKS HAD HIM A WHILE. THEIR PSY-OPS CAN FLIP ANYONE. BRAINWASHING... MAYBE WORSE.
LEMME ASK YOU SOME QUESTIONS. I CAN USUALLY SNIFF OUT WHEN SOMEONE'S LYIN'.
IT'S OKAY. I DON'T MIND...

THE HELL ARE YOU--
HOLO, THAT'S WHAT I'M TALKIN' ABOUT! FORREST SAW YOU!
VIC, WE WERE JUST TALKING!
Y'KNOW WHAT? WHEN CRAP GETS STIRRED UP, FORREST'S ALWAYS IN THE MIDDLE OF IT.
WHAT'RE YOU SAYING ABOUT MY BROTHER? YOU KNOW HE'S--
SNIKT
WE AIN'T DONE, RUNT.

NOW!
BROK
RRRNNCHH

TARGETS IDENTIFIED.
MUTANTS. SURRENDER OR DIE.
BRRBOOOOOOM

FORREST! WHAT HAPPENED TO YOU?
NOTHING THAT WON'T HAPPEN TO YOU.
NO WAY AM I GOING BACK. I'LL DIE FIRST.
OR BETTER YET... THEY WILL!

THEY'RE ROBOTS! MY ILLUSIONS WON'T WORK ON THEM!
SO DON'T WASTE YER TIME. THEY GOT BACKUP-- HUMAN SOLDIERS SOMEWHERE.
TAKE 'EM OUTTA THE EQUATION.

MR. HARTFIELD, I HAVE A SHOT. AWAITING YOUR ORDER--

FIRE! OPEN FIRE!
WHAT'S WRONG WITH YOU?
WHAT THE HELL--?

I'M SEEING *YOU* IN THE KILL ZONE, SIR. NO TARGETS, JUST *OUR MEN!*
HOLD FIRE. *HOLD FIRE!* THAT ILLUSIONIST WITCH IS MAKING US SE THINGS!
WE DON'T NEED FRIENDLY CASUALTIES. RETREAT AND LET THE ROBOTS DO THEIR JOB.
YETI--WE CAN'T FIND YER BROTHER IF WE'RE ALL DEAD. GOTTA TAKE OUT THE ROBOTS...WHICH MEANS FINDIN' THEIR WEAK SPOTS.
FOOM
C'MERE. I WANNA SEE IF SOMETHING'LL WORK.

NOT BAD.
GOTTA REMEMBER THIS.

HAS TO BE
RAIN IN HERE
MEWHERE...
ERROR!
PU DAMAGE!
ERROR!
TARGETING MUTANT... LETHAL FORCE AUTHORIZED...
ERROR ERROR ERROR
THEIR BRAINS ARE IN THE BACK O'THEIR HEADS! HIT 'EM THERE!
SQUAARRRKK--
W D'YOU LIKE
LOGAN NOW,
METEOR?
GOTTA ADMIT, HE'S GOOD. WE MIGHT JUST HAVE A CHANCE.

FORREST!
HOLO, C'MERE. WE GOTTA GET YOU UNDERCOVER.
AND THIS AIN'T ME BEIN' PROTECTIVE. YOU'RE OUR BEST WEAPON AGAINST THE SOLDIERS, SO MOVE.
IT'S NOT THE SOLDIERS YOU NEED TO WORRY ABOUT.
RUN, HOLO.
RUN!
AWRIGHT, EVERYBODY PULL TOGETHER! LIKE WE PRACTICED! WE WORK A TEAM, WE CAN MAK IT THROUGH THIS!
MAY WA TO RETHI THAT PLA

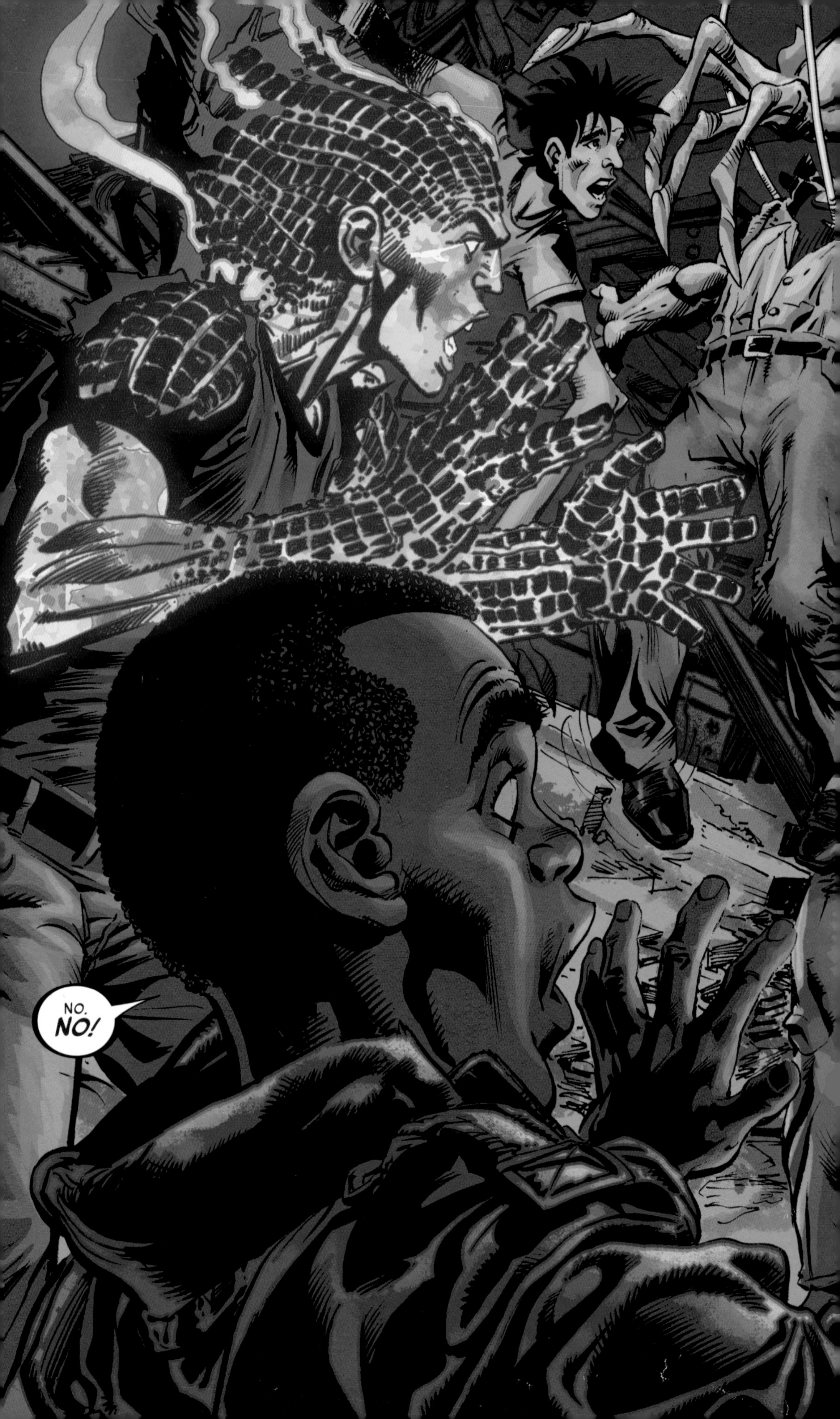
NO.
NO!

THERE'S BEEN SOME ROSTER CHANGES.

NOW I GET THEY CALL YOU US 'CAUSE YOU E IN PEOPLE. TAKE OVER. LIKE A DISEASE.
ALL THOSE REASONS. AND ONE MORE. THOSE I INFECT TEND TO DIE.
YOU SHOULD BE HONORED. WHICHEVER ONE OF YOU KILLS THE OTHER GETS TO BE MY MOUNT. FOREVER.
ITH YOUR HEALING TORS, I'LL NEVER USE OU UP. I'LL HAVE A PERMANENT BODY AT LAST.
DAMN IT, CREED, FIGHT HIM!
RYTHING'S LIN' APART OUND US!
METEOR, NO!

CREED, THIS ISN'T YOU! FIGHT IT!
RARRRGH
THIS IS WHAT YOU REALLY WANT, ISN'T IT?
TO BE NORMAL?
WHAT?!
STOP. STOP!
THIS CAN'T BE WHAT YOU WANT.
GET OUT OF MY HEAD!

OST NTROL, 'T YA, EAK?
SHKKKK
GGNAAAA!
I DID LIKE YOU TAUGHT ME. GOT IN HIS HEAD.
YOU WERE AMAZIN', BABE. I AIN'T NEVER GONNA FORGET THIS.
H-HOW TRUE...
...YOU NEVER WILL.
WHAT? NO--
VICTOR, WHAT ARE YOU--
CREED!
LOGAN, STOP ME, I'M NOT--

NOOOO!
SHUNK
H-HEH...HCCH...
V-VIC...?
HOLLY...?

NO. NO.
HE SAID 'D BE OKAY. SAID YOU'D E OKAY!
HANG IN HERE, KID. KID?!
--
IS IS YOUR FAULT!
YOU! YOU AND YOUR DAMN CRUSADE!
YOU DID THIS!
I...
YOU'RE RIGHT.
GET HER TO A DOCTOR.
ALL'A YOU, GET THE HELL OUT!
I STARTED THIS.
I'M GONNA FINISH IT.
BUT MR. LOGAN...

SQUARRKK
YOU SAID WE GOTTA FIGHT. YOU SAID WE CAN'T EVER GIVE UP!
SHUT UP AND GET MOVIN', BOMB.
I'M STAYING. YOU AND ME, TO THE END.
WE'RE ALL WITH YOU.
STUPID KIDS. YOU REALLY THI YOU'RE ANY USE ME? YOU THINK Y EVER WERE?
TRAINING'S OVER. YOU FAILED!
NOW GET OUTTA MY SIGHT.

MR. LOGAN... MY BROTHER.
GO. HE NEEDS YA. GET 'IM OUTTA HERE.
BUT IF YOU GOT TIME FOR ONE LAST LIFT...
RRRRAAAGGHHH!
GIVE 'EM HELL.
SHHRRNNCHH
ALERT. FUEL LEAK.
FWOOOMF

IT'S ARMAGEDDON IN THERE. THE SENTINEL ROBOTS ARE A TOTAL LOSS.
WHAT ABOUT THE MUTANTS?
NO ONE'S GETTING OUT OF THAT.
NO!
KYLE, DON'T!
AGENT DANSIG, ARE YOU INSANE?
DAMN IT, THEY'RE MY SONS!
JAMIE! JOSEF! PLEASE I'M SORRY! I'LL GET YOU OUT OF HERE!
OH, THANK GOD. I THOUGHT YOU'D BE SAFE... I'VE BEEN SUCH A FOOL.
DAD!
GO WITH YOUR SONS, KYLE DANSIG. YOUR COLLEAGUES WILL SEE YOU DIE IN THE FLAMES...
...OR SO THEY WILL BELIEVE. THEY WILL NOT LOOK FOR YOU. ANY OF YOU.
RUN. HIDE. LIVE.
EVERYTHING'S GOING TO BE OKAY NOW, RIGHT?

T'S GONNA OKAY, HOLLY. GET YOU TO HOSPITAL.
W-WE'RE IN THE MIDDLE...OF NOWHERE...
THERE'S A ROAD. JUST TTA PRAY A CAR OMES. WE CAN MAKE IT IF...
RRRRRR
YES!
HEY!
OUT.
HOLD ON, BABY. JUST A LITTLE LONGER. I SWEAR TO YOU...
...EVERYTHING'S GONNA BE FINE.
MR. CREED? SHE WAS VERY BADLY HURT...
...BUT SHE'LL PULL THROUGH.
OH, THANK GOD.
IF I'D LOST YOU, HOLLY...I...I DON'T KNOW WHAT I WOULDA--
SHH. I KNOW. DON'T THINK ABOUT THAT NOW...

"...WE'VE GOT THE REST OF OUR LIVES AHEAD OF US."
WHAT ABOUT LOGAN AND THE OTHERS?
SCREW 'EM. TO HELL WITH THE WHOLE DAMN WORLD. WE TRIED TO BE HEROES AND IT ALMOST GOT US KILLED. FROM HERE ON OUT...

"...WE LIVE FOR US."

IT'S BEEN A GOOD LIFE, VICTOR. HASN'T IT?
BETTER'N I EVER THOUGHT A GUY LIKE ME COULD HOPE FOR.
THE BEST.

HOLD ON TO THAT, VIC. MAK THIS WHAT YO REMEMBER.
HUH?
WHAT ARE YOU--

-WHAT HELL--
IT DOESN'T HAVE TO MATTER ANY LESS.
IT'S AS REAL...AS YOU...
...MAKE IT...
H-HOLLY? WHAT...
...NO...
NNNAAAAGGH!

HOURS LATER.

LOGAN.

DON'T. I'M TOLD THIS GUN CAN KILL EVEN YOU.
I THINK THEY MIGHT'VE BEEN OVERCONFIDENT, BUT IT CAN SURE AS HELL PUT YOU DOWN.
AND IF YOU'LL **THINK** FOR TWO SECONDS YOU'LL KNOW I HAD **NO PART** IN APPROVING THIS MISSION... **OR** CARRYING IT OUT.

ANYONE MAKE IT?
I SAW MOST OF THEM DIE. I'M SORRY.
Y'KNOW WHAT THEY CALLED ME IN THE SERVICE, DUNCAN? THE WOLVERINE. 'CAUSE I STAND AND FIGHT NO MATTER HOW BIG THE ENEMY...HOW BAD THE ODDS.
AFTER ALL THESE YEARS'A BEIN' A MERCENARY, I THOUGHT I FINALLY FOUND A CAUSE. SOMEWHERE TO BELONG.
ALL I DID WAS GET A BUNCH'A KIDS KILLED. FOR NOTHING.
MAYBE NOT. THIS WAS A DISASTER FOR US, TOO. BILLIONS WASTED WITH SQUAT TO SHOW FOR IT.
EVERYONE INVOLVED HAS EN AXED.--EXCEPT E, BECAUSE I SAID WAS STUPID FROM E START. YOU'RE OKING AT THE NEW DEPARTMENT OF MUTANT AFFAIRS.
I'M MAKING POLICY NOW. THE BRASS DOESN'T CARE WHAT IT IS, AS LONG AS IT'S CHEAP. MOST OF THE MUTANTS IN THE COUNTRY DIED LAST NIGHT. HOW WE HANDLE THE NEXT GENERATION IS UP TO ME.
IT CAN BE UP TO YOU, TOO, LOGAN. IF YOU'LL WORK WITH ME.
I'M DONE TRYIN' TO BE SOMETHIN' I'M NOT.
TIME I FACED UP TO IT. ALL I DO IS KILL.
AND I'M THE BEST THERE IS AT WHAT I DO.

NEW YORK.
COME ON, BOLIVAR. BILLIONS DOWN THE DRAIN BUILDING ROBOTS WITH GLARING DESIGN FLAWS...
FAIR OR NOT, THE DISASTER'S BEING BLAMED ON YOU. EVERYONE IN WASHINGTON JUST LOST YOUR PHONE NUMBER.
IT'S LIKE THAT, IS IT? FINE! THIS ISN'T A PUNISHMENT. I WAS JUST SET FREE!
I'LL DO IT MY WAY. PUT MY OWN MONEY INTO IT...EVERY PENNY I HAVE.
UNLIKE THEM, I LEARN FROM MY MISTAKES.
WE'LL SHOW THEM, SON. WE'LL SHOW THEM ALL.
THIS ISN'T THE END OF THE SENTINELS.
IT'S JUST THE BEGINNING.

FAIRFAX, VIRGINIA.
I AGREE IT'S A GENEROUS PENSION. IT'S JUST NOT ENOUGH.
I UNDERSTAND I WAS IN CHARGE OF THE MUTANT PROGRAM. I UNDERSTAND I HAVE TO FALL ON MY SWORD. BUT YOU SHOULD UNDERSTAND THAT I'M NOT GOING EASILY.
I DIDN'T MAKE DECISIONS IN A VACUUM. WHAT I KNOW COULD PANIC THE NATION...AND END CAREERS. INCLUDING YOURS, SENATOR.
TRY TO PLAY HARDBALL WITH ME, YOU SONS OF--
HARTFIELD.
YOU!
LISTEN TO ME. I CAN MAKE YOU RICH. I CAN GIVE YOU ANYTHING YOU WANT.
YOU ALREADY TOOK THAT. AIN'T NOTHING LEFT I WANT.
EXCEPT ONE THING.
I DON'T EVEN NEED THESE FOR THAT.
EEEAAAAGGHH

RUMORS PERSIST OF INVOLVEMENT BY PEOP WITH EXTRAORDINAR ABILITIES--WHAT SOM CONSPIRACY THEORISTS C MUTANTS. THIS SPECULAT CENTERS ON THE MILITA CORDON THAT REMAINS EFFECT AROUND THE AR
MY POOR, FOOLISH FRIENDS. AS PROMISED, I DRINK TO YOUR MEMORY...AND THE PASSING OF YOUR RECKLESS DREAM.
AND NOW THE HUMANS WILL WANT BLOOD.
THEY WILL TRY TO DESTROY US BEFORE WE ARE STRONG ENOUGH TO OPPOSE THEM. SO WE MUST BECOME STRONG ENOUGH.
I PROMISE YOU THAT THE NEXT TIME, HUMANITY WILL NOT FACE CHILDREN O THE BATTLEFIELD. THEY WILL BE MEETING AN ARMY. A PEOPLE UNITED.
A BROTHERHOOD.

OTHER
TTLE.
ALBERTA, CANADA.
HONEY, YOU ALREADY HAD ENOUGH TO KILL MOST MEN.
I WISH IT WERE THAT EASY.
AIN'T GONNA BE.
CREED.
HOLLY--
YEAH.
DO WHAT YOU CAME HERE FOR. I AIN'T GONNA STOP YOU.
NOT HERE TO KILL YOU.
FAR AS I'M CONCERNED, YOU CAN STAY JUST LIKE THIS.
BUT I'M GONNA MAKE YOU A PROMISE. YOU EVER FIND ANYTHING--ANYBODY MAKES LIFE WORTH LIVING AGAIN--
I'LL BE THERE.

THIS MAN DRINKS ON ME.
AS MUCH AS HE WANTS.
CREED!
DAMN IT, CREED!
MR. LOGAN?
WE REPRESENT A GOVERNMENT PROGRAM CALLED WEAPON X. WE ARE HERE TO OFFER YOU THE OPPORTUNITY TO SERVE YOUR COUNTRY.
WE BELIEVE THAT YOU COULD BE MADE INTO THE PERFECT SOLDIER.
BUT TRUTH BE TOLD, THERE IS A VERY GOOD CHANCE IT WILL KILL YOU.

SIGN ME UP.

WESTCHESTER.
POK POK POK
GOD REST HER SOUL, YOUR MOTHER WOULD BE SO PROUD TO SEE THIS.
SCHOOL
NOT THAT SHE WOULDN'T BE PROUD OF YOUR EDUCATION OF COURSE, OR YOUR MILITAR SERVICE. BUT USING THE FAMILY FORTUNE TO GIVE BACK WAS HER TRUE PASSION.
STILL, I FEEL I MUST ASK...THIS WILL BE A SIGNIFICANT INVESTMENT, CHARLES. ARE YOU SURE THIS IS WHAT YOU WANT?
QUITE SURE. I'LL ADMIT, THERE WERE TIMES I HAD DOUBTS. BUT NOW I REALIZE I WAS BEING SELFISH. UNTRUE TO MOTHER...AND MYSELF.
XAVIER'S SCHOOL FOR GIFTED
EDMUND BURKE SAID ALL THAT IS NECESSARY FOR EVIL TO TRIUMPH IS FOR GOOD MEN TO DO NOTHING.
IT'S TIME FOR ME TO DO SOMETHING.
XAVIER'S SCHOOL FOR GIFTED YOUNGSTERS

FIRST X-MEN: CHILDREN OF THE ATOM VARIANT COVERS

FIRST X-MEN #1 BY NEAL ADAMS

FIRST X-MEN #1 BY NEAL ADAMS

FIRST X-MEN #1 BY RYAN STEGMAN

FIRST X-MEN #1 BY RYAN STEGMAN

FIRST X-MEN #2 BY MIKE DEODATO JR.

FIRST X-MEN #3 BY SHANE DAVIS

FIRST X-MEN #4 BY DANIEL ACUNA

FIRST X-MEN #5 BY ADAM KUBERT

AVENGERS VS X-MEN
MARVEL

OF THE SUPERMEN

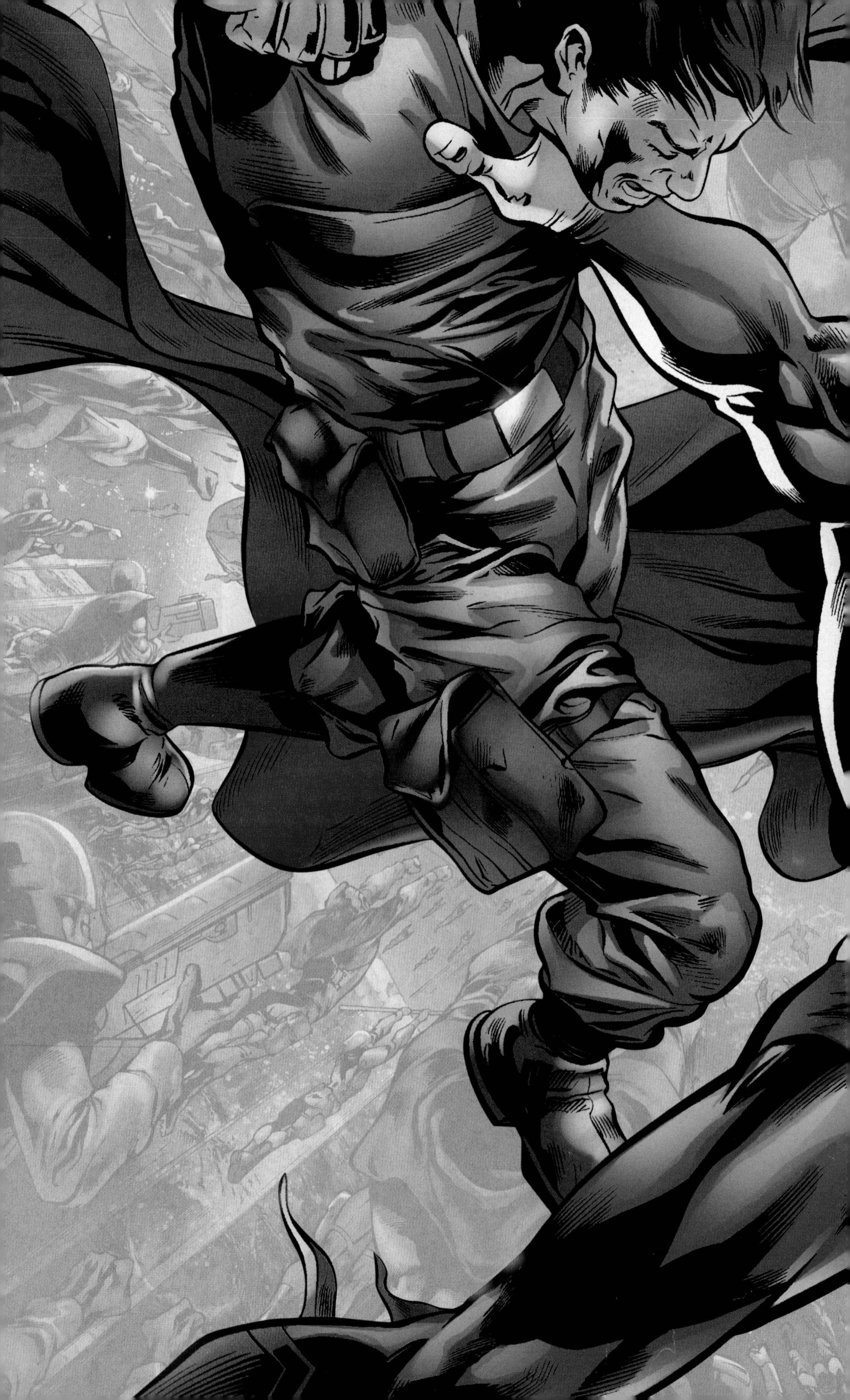

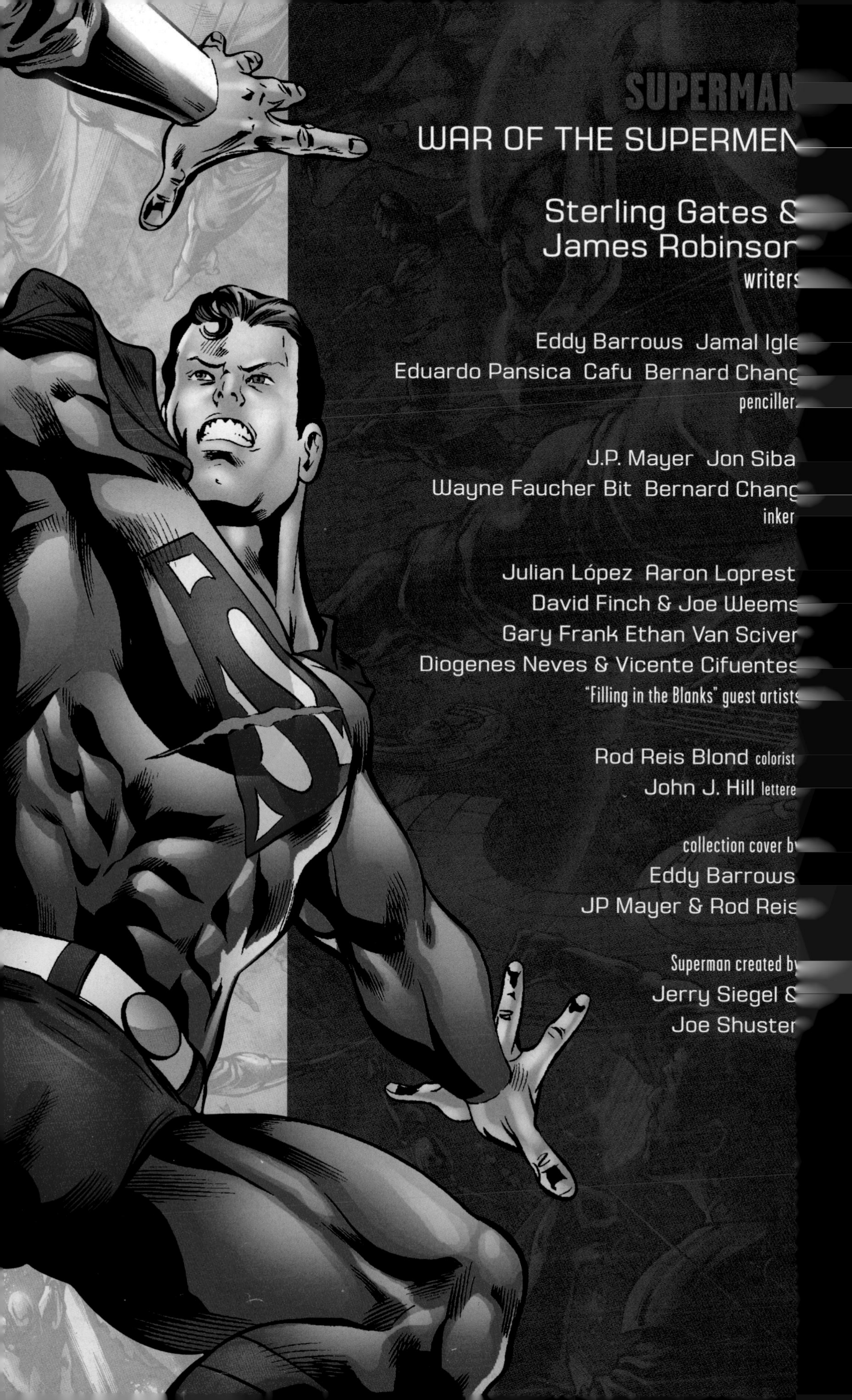

SUPERMAN
WAR OF THE SUPERMEN

Sterling Gates &
James Robinson
writers

Eddy Barrows Jamal Igle
Eduardo Pansica Cafu Bernard Chang
pencillers

J.P. Mayer Jon Siba
Wayne Faucher Bit Bernard Chang
inkers

Julian López Aaron Lopresti
David Finch & Joe Weems
Gary Frank Ethan Van Sciver
Diogenes Neves & Vicente Cifuentes
"Filling in the Blanks" guest artists

Rod Reis Blond colorists
John J. Hill letterer

collection cover by
Eddy Barrows
JP Mayer & Rod Reis

Superman created by
Jerry Siegel &
Joe Shuster

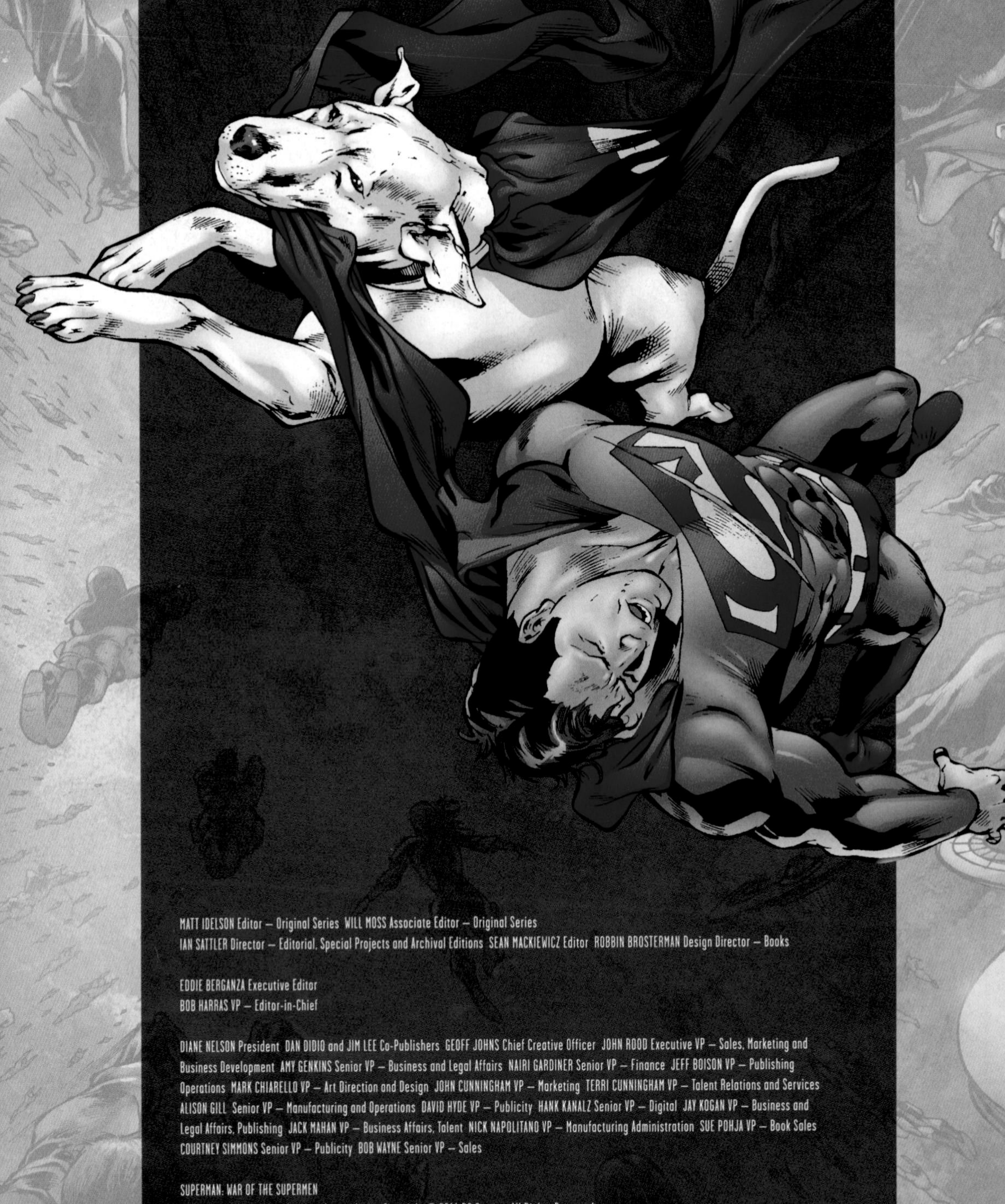

MATT IDELSON Editor – Original Series WILL MOSS Associate Editor – Original Series
IAN SATTLER Director – Editorial, Special Projects and Archival Editions SEAN MACKIEWICZ Editor ROBBIN BROSTERMAN Design Director – Books

EDDIE BERGANZA Executive Editor
BOB HARRAS VP – Editor-in-Chief

DIANE NELSON President DAN DIDIO and JIM LEE Co-Publishers GEOFF JOHNS Chief Creative Officer JOHN ROOD Executive VP – Sales, Marketing and Business Development AMY GENKINS Senior VP – Business and Legal Affairs NAIRI GARDINER Senior VP – Finance JEFF BOISON VP – Publishing Operations MARK CHIARELLO VP – Art Direction and Design JOHN CUNNINGHAM VP – Marketing TERRI CUNNINGHAM VP – Talent Relations and Services ALISON GILL Senior VP – Manufacturing and Operations DAVID HYDE VP – Publicity HANK KANALZ Senior VP – Digital JAY KOGAN VP – Business and Legal Affairs, Publishing JACK MAHAN VP – Business Affairs, Talent NICK NAPOLITANO VP – Manufacturing Administration SUE POHJA VP – Book Sales COURTNEY SIMMONS Senior VP – Publicity BOB WAYNE Senior VP – Sales

SUPERMAN: WAR OF THE SUPERMEN

DC Comics, 1700 Broadway, New York, NY 10019
A Warner Bros. Entertainment Company
Printed by RR Donnelley, Salem, VA, USA. 12/16/11. First Printing.
ISBN: 978-1-4012-3187-3

Fiber used in this product line meets the sourcing requirements of the SFI program.
www.sfiprogram.org SGS-SFI/COC-US10/81072

PROLOGUE Cover by EDDY BARROWS, J.P. MAYER & ROD REIS

ON THE FAR SIDE OF THE SUN--MILLIONS OF MILES FROM EARTH--IS A PLANET OF MY PEOPLE.
NEW KRYPTON.
I CAME HERE A YEAR AGO TO ENSURE MY PEOPLE WOULD **THRIVE**.
TO KEEP THEM FROM MAKING MISTAKES.
AFTER A YEAR, THEY'VE MADE THE BIGGEST MISTAKE OF **ALL**.
THEY'VE PUT THEIR TRUST IN THE **WRONG** MAN--
--ZOD!

KRYPTONIAN MILITARY INSTALLATION KV-426.
ONE MILE BENEATH NEW KRYPTON'S SURFACE.
KAL-EL.
YOUR COMMENTS ARE NOTED, EL, BUT AS I TOLD YOU WHEN YOU GAVE UP YOUR POSITION IN MY MILITARY--
--YOUR OPINIONS DON'T MATTER TO ME NOW.

JUDGING BY YOUR OVERLY DRAMATIC ENTRANCE, I'M GUESSING YOU'RE NOT HERE TO RE-ENLIST IN MY ARMY.
RE-ENLIST?
I'M HERE BECAUSE YOU JUST TOLD ONE-HUNDRED THOUSAND KRYPTONIANS WE'RE DECLARING WAR ON EARTH!
I'M HERE TO SHUT YOU--AND ALL OF THIS--DOWN.

MY OPINIONS AREN'T WHAT YOU SHOULD BE WORRIED ABOUT, GENERAL.

GENERAL ZOD!
ARE YOU ALL RIGHT?
HHH.
YOUR LACK OF DISCIPLINE ALWAYS SEEMS TO SHINE THROUGH, EL...

...AND I TIRE OF UNDISCIPLINED PEOPLE.
URSA, PLEASE SHOW "SUPERMAN" WHAT A PRECISE STRIKE IS LIKE.

GLADLY.
AAAAAH!
...KRYPTONITE... KNIFE...?
BEAUTIFUL, ISN'T IT?
IT HURTS TO HOLD, BUT IT ALWAYS GIVES ME SUCH SATISFACTION.

NOT ANYMORE.
SSSSS
KSSSHH
AAAGH--!
NOW, GENERAL...
...WHERE WERE WE?
I BELIEVE YOU WERE SURRENDERING, KAL-EL.
VERY FUNNY, ZOD. I--
...WHAT--?

HRRRRR--!
NNNN!

THANK YOU, NON.
I'LL STOP YOU, ZOD! I'LL--
YES, YOU'VE DONE A GREAT JOB THUS FAR.
I WON'T LET YOU TURN THIS PLANET INTO YOUR PERSONAL WAR MACHINE--
WHEN HAVE I HEARD THAT BEFORE? OH, YES. WHEN YOU FIRST CAME HERE...
...EVEN GOING SO FAR AS TO RENOUNCE EARTH SO YOU COULD "SAVE NEW KRYPTON FROM THE EVILS OF ZOD." TO HELP THE PLANET GET THE LEADER IT DESERVES?
THAT'S WHAT YOU DO, ISN'T IT...APPEAR, THE GREAT AND POWERFUL FIXER. SPEECHES AND SMILES AND SUPER STRENGTH.
NOT HERE, THOUGH. NO SUPERMAN HERE. YOU WEREN'T SUPER.
NOT WHEN THE YELLOW SUN HAS LEVELED THE PLAYING FIELD AND MADE US ALL THE SAME.
YOU'RE JUST ONE OF ONE-HUNDRED THOUSAND, AL WITH POWERS LIKE YOU.

YOU CAME HERE TO PROTECT THE PEOPLE FROM ME? TO MONITOR ME?
MAYBE YOU SHOULD HAVE SPENT MORE TIME WATCHING THE PEOPLE, EL...TRULY PROTECTING THEM, LIKE I'VE DONE.
I KNOW IT MUST EAT AT YOU... THAT I DIDN'T WIN NEW KRYPTON'S LOVE THROUGH GUILE OR TRICKERY.
I EARNED IT.
AND ALL THAT TIME YOU WERE WATCHING ME, RIGHT? I SEE THAT NOW...THAT'S THE REASON YOU KEPT ME CLOSE.
THAT'S WHY YOU MADE ME A COMMANDER IN THE ARMY.

NO, I HAD YOU JOIN THE MILITARY GUILD FOR A MUCH MORE SPECIFIC AND IMPORTANT REASON.
RED SHARD WAS YOUR DIRECT COMMAND, OF COURSE, BUT THE MASS TRAINING EXERCISES YOU OVERSAW... SHOWING THE SOLDIERS OF NEW KRYPTON HOW TO BETTER HANDLE THEIR NEW POWERS...

...IT WAS YOUR YEARS OF PRIOR EXPERIENCE THAT TURNED MY ARMY INTO THE CONSUMMATE FORCE IT NEEDED TO BECOME.

AND YOU'VE BEEN PLANNING TO ATTACK EARTH THIS WHOLE TIME, RIGHT?
THE ARMADA I UNCOVERED. CLASSIFIED AREAS I COULDN'T BREACH. THE WAY THE ARMY WAS TRAINED...INDEED, THE WAY I HELPED TRAIN THEM.
IT WAS STUPID OF ME TO HOPE YOU'D CHANGE FROM THE MAN YOU WERE, BUT--
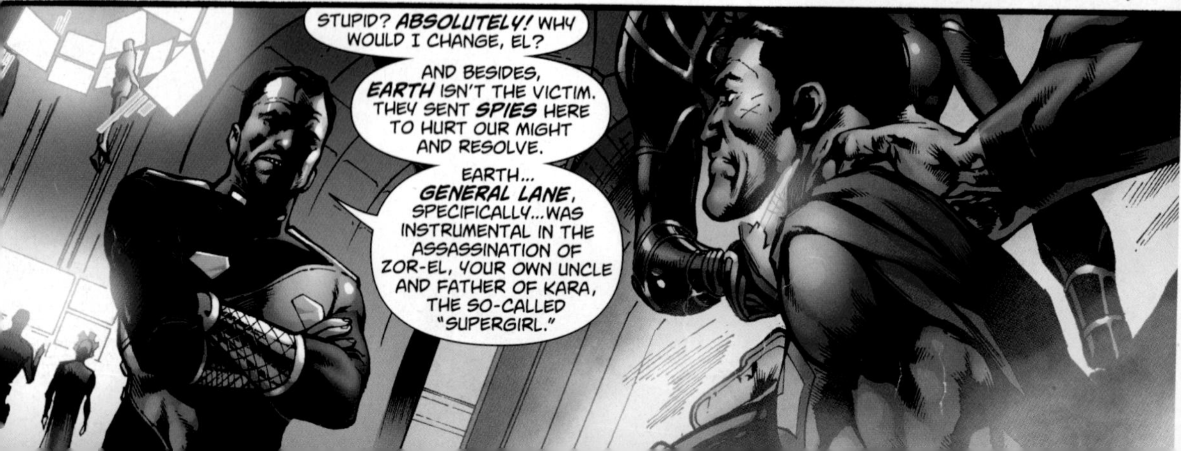
STUPID? ABSOLUTELY! WHY WOULD I CHANGE, EL?
AND BESIDES, EARTH ISN'T THE VICTIM. THEY SENT SPIES HERE TO HURT OUR MIGHT AND RESOLVE.
EARTH... GENERAL LANE, SPECIFICALLY...WAS INSTRUMENTAL IN THE ASSASSINATION OF ZOR-EL, YOUR OWN UNCLE AND FATHER OF KARA, THE SO-CALLED "SUPERGIRL."

I HAD A SPY WITHIN LANE'S ENCLAVE, AND BEFORE SHE WAS UNCOVERED AND KILLED, SHE COMMUNICATED TO ME THAT EARTH'S FORCES ARE MOBILIZING TO ATTACK US.
I'M NOT TOTALLY WITHOUT CAUSE.
BUT NO... I HAVEN'T CHANGED, PARTICULARLY IN ONE REGARD. I'M STILL THE MAN WHO SWORE REVENGE ON JOR-EL'S HOUSE AND YOURS. THE HOUSE OF EL.
SO DON'T FOR A MOMENT THINK THIS ISN'T PERSONAL AS WELL.
I'M GOING TO LEVEL YOUR ADOPTED PLANET AND KICK THE ASH FROM THE CHARRED BONES OF THE DEAD IN YOUR FACE.
AND BETTER YET, I'LL FIND WHOEVER YOU LOVE THE MOST ON EARTH, RIP THAT PERSON APART BEFORE YOUR EYES...
...AND YOU'LL BE POWERLESS TO STOP ME.
ONE THING YOU SAID, ZOD... EARLIER...WAS WRONG.
YES? AND WHAT WOULD THAT BE?
I NEVER RENOUNCED EARTH!

DON'T YOU UNDERSTAND?

A WAR WOULD MEAN THE END OF BOTH WORLDS!
I WON'T LET THAT HAPPEN!
I'M CURIOUS TO KNOW HOW YOU'LL STOP ME, "SUPERMAN"...

"...WHEN I'VE ALREADY GIVEN THE ORDER TO ATTACK!"

EARTH.
METROPOLIS.
YESTERDAY.
LOIS LANE
GEN LANE
NEW KRYPTON
WHAT DOES ZOD KNOW?
CODENAME: ASSASSIN? ATLAS?
RUSH
LUCY = KRYPTONIAN?
LOIS LANE
C:>//DAILYPLANET/
securelogin/loislane

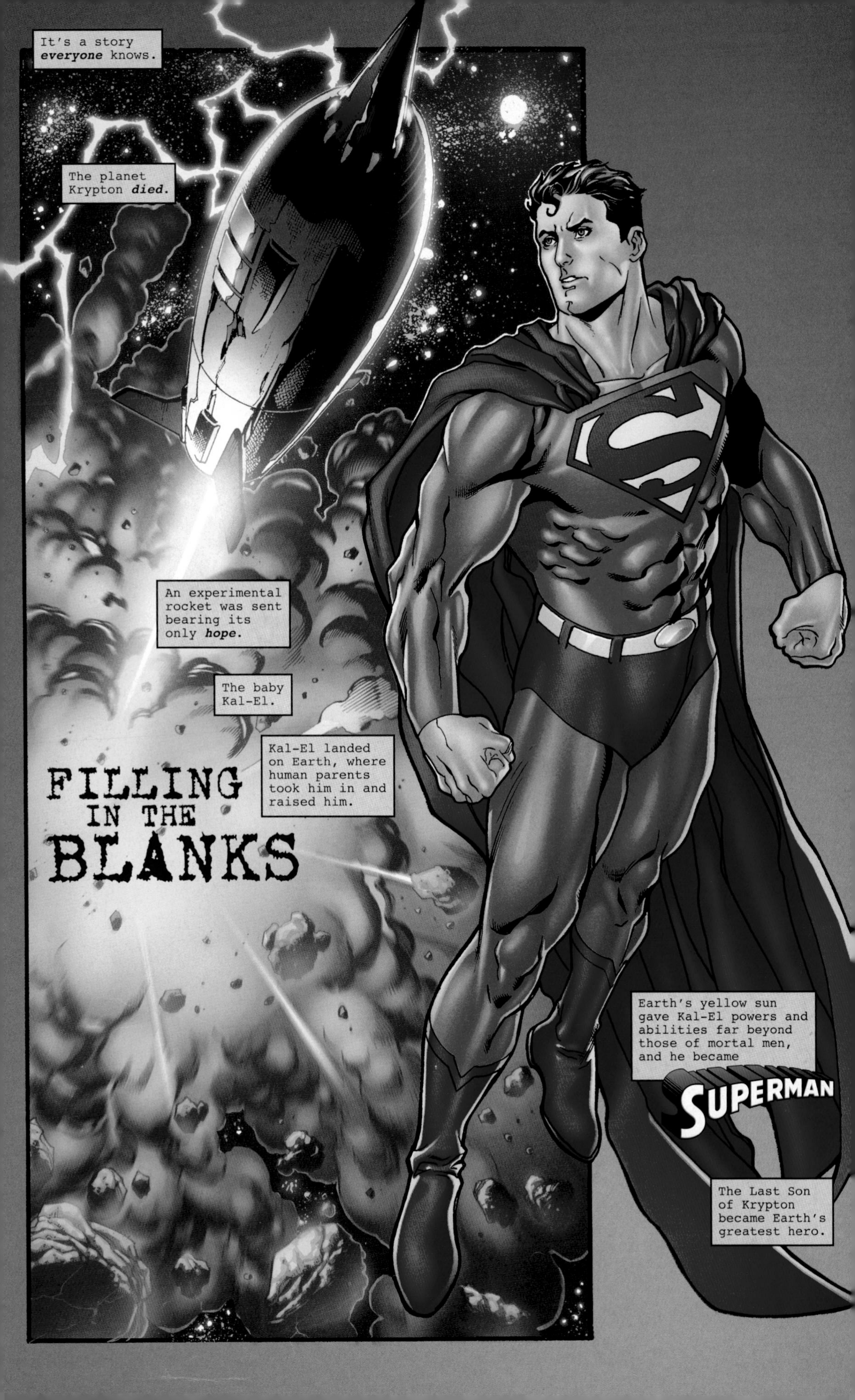
It's a story *everyone* knows.
The planet Krypton *died*.
An experimental rocket was sent bearing its only *hope*.
The baby Kal-El.
FILLING IN THE BLANKS
Kal-El landed on Earth, where human parents took him in and raised him.
Earth's yellow sun gave Kal-El powers and abilities far beyond those of mortal men, and he became
SUPERMAN
The Last Son of Krypton became Earth's greatest hero.

Years later, Superman found he wasn't *alone* in the universe.
His cousin *Kara* also survived Krypton's destruction, as did a handful of Kryptonian criminals imprisoned in the Phantom Zone.
During an encounter with the villain Brainiac, *Superman* and *Supergirl* discovered the long-lost bottled city of Kandor--
--*stolen* from Krypton prior to its destruction.
Superman *re-enlarged* the city on *Earth*...

...and a race thought long dead *lived* again.
But these 100,000 alien immigrants did not find Earth as welcoming a home as Superman and Supergirl did.
Humans invaded their city, and tragedy befell them once more.
Their leader, Zor-El--Supergirl's *father*--was killed.
They decided to *leave* Earth. Using highly evolved science, Zor-El's wife Alura created a *new* planet for her people--
NEW KRYPTON
With no one strong enough to *defend* them, the Kryptonians turned to a man they thought they could trust.
A man who had once been a *hero* on Krypton, but had been *imprisoned* in the Phantom Zone for his crimes--

--General Zod.
Alura, now leader of the Kryptonians, set him free.
Knowing Zod for the criminal he is, Superman made the hardest decision of his life.
He knew Zod wasn't to be trusted. He had to get closer to Zod, to watch him...
...so he moved to New Krypton and joined Zod's Army.

But Superman hadn't left Earth without *protection*.
Superboy and Krypto--
--Nightwing and Flamebird--
--the Guardian--
--Mon-El--
--and Steel *all* stepped in to fill the gap left as Earth's greatest *champion* kept a watchful eye on General Zod.

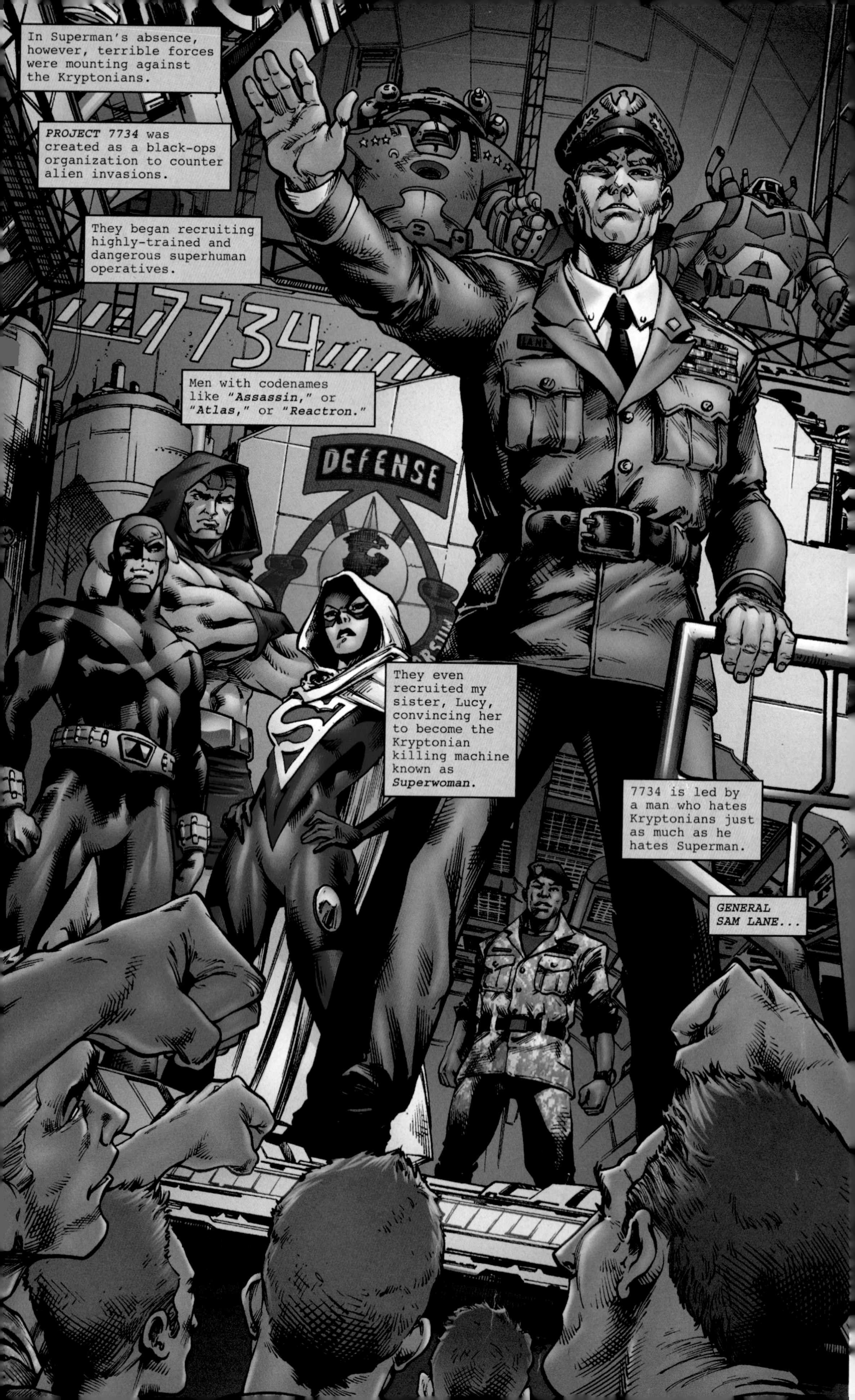
In Superman's absence, however, terrible forces were mounting against the Kryptonians.
PROJECT 7734 was created as a black-ops organization to counter alien invasions.
They began recruiting highly-trained and dangerous superhuman operatives.
7734
Men with codenames like "*Assassin*," or "*Atlas*," or "*Reactron*."
DEFENSE
They even recruited my sister, Lucy, convincing her to become the Kryptonian killing machine known as *Superwoman*.
7734 is led by a man who hates Kryptonians just as much as he hates Superman.
GENERAL SAM LANE...

...my father.
This story doesn't have an ending yet. My father has gone to great lengths to silence *anyone* who's tried to look too deeply.
Daily Planet photojournalist Jimmy Olsen began investigating on his own. They found his body at the bottom of Metropolis Harbor two days later. More innocent blood on my father's hands.
DNG
Working on this story…and with Superman off-planet…I worry about my *own* safety.
But you can't *suppress* the truth, even when it *hurts*. And someone out there knows *more*.
Someone can fill in the blanks that I haven't yet.
Blanks like where Project 7734 is based. Like *what* their anti-Kryptonian agenda entails. Like *when*--not *if*--they're going to strike.
Daily Planet Editor-In-Chief Perry White once had the courage to stand up to Lex Luthor when no one else would.
It was his bravery in reporting the truth that made the Planet great. That made the Planet my *inspiration* growing up.
I'm standing up for what's right today, and I'm going to *expose* my father for what he is if it's the last thing I
I'VE GOT *INFORMATION* FOR YOU, MS. LANE--
WHMP

--BUT I'M GOING TO NEED YOUR HELP PUTTING SOME OF IT TOGETHER.
JIMMY?!
BUT-- WE THOUGHT YOU WERE--
DEAD? NO, MS. LANE. NATASHA IRONS--STEEL'S NIECE--HAS BEEN HELPING ME STAY UNDERCOVER AND OUT OF SIGHT.
SHE WAS HELPING ME WORK ON A STORY. A STORY THAT'S BIGGER THAN ANYTHING I'VE EVER WORKED ON.
TOGETHER, WE DISCOVERED HORRIBLE INFORMATION ABOUT PROJECT 7734. UNIMAGINABLE THINGS.
NATASHA'S GONE MISSING, I THINK BECAUSE OF WHAT WE'VE LEARNED. DO YOU WANT TO HEAR ABOUT GENERAL LANE?
DO YOU WANT TO HEAR THE TRUTH ABOUT YOUR FATHER?
ABSOLUTELY.

PART 1: THE BATTLE FOR NEW KRYPTON Cover by EDDY BARROWS, J.P. MAYER & ROD REIS

"WHATEVER YOU WERE PLANNING, 'SUPERMAN'...
"...WHATEVER HOPES YOU HAD OF STOPPING THIS...
"...ARE STILLBORN.
"MY ORDER HAS BEEN GIVEN.
"THE ARMY OF NEW KRYPTON IS ALREADY ON ITS WAY TO EARTH.
"THE WAR HAS STARTED."

NEW KRYPTON.
I **WON'T** LET YOU DO THIS, ZOD.
I'LL NEVER ALLOW--
ALLOW?

YOU'RE IN **NO** POSITION TO "ALLOW." I'LL HAVE YOUR WORLD **OBLITERATED** INSIDE OF TWO HOURS.
YOU HAVE **NO HOPE**. NO HOPE TO STOP ME, AND NO HOPE OF SEEING YOUR PLANET OR ITS PEOPLE AGAIN.
YOU'RE **WRONG**.

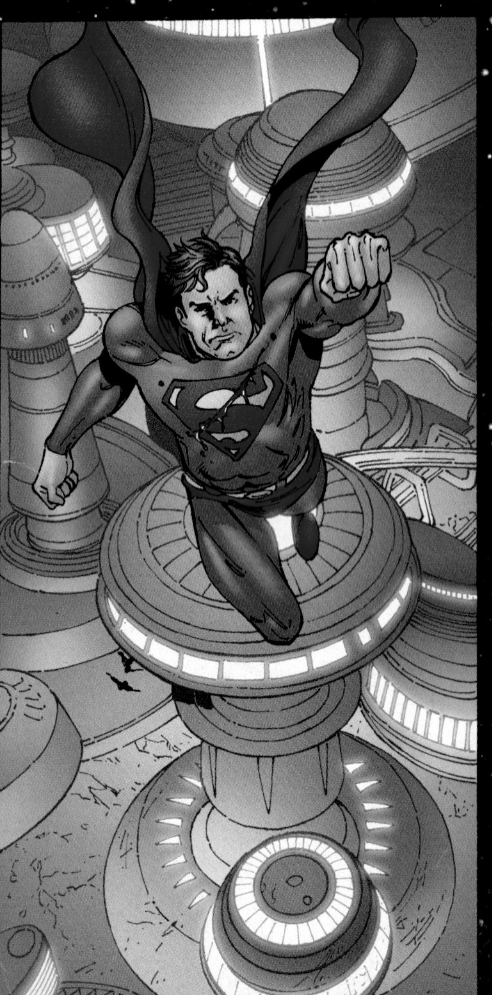

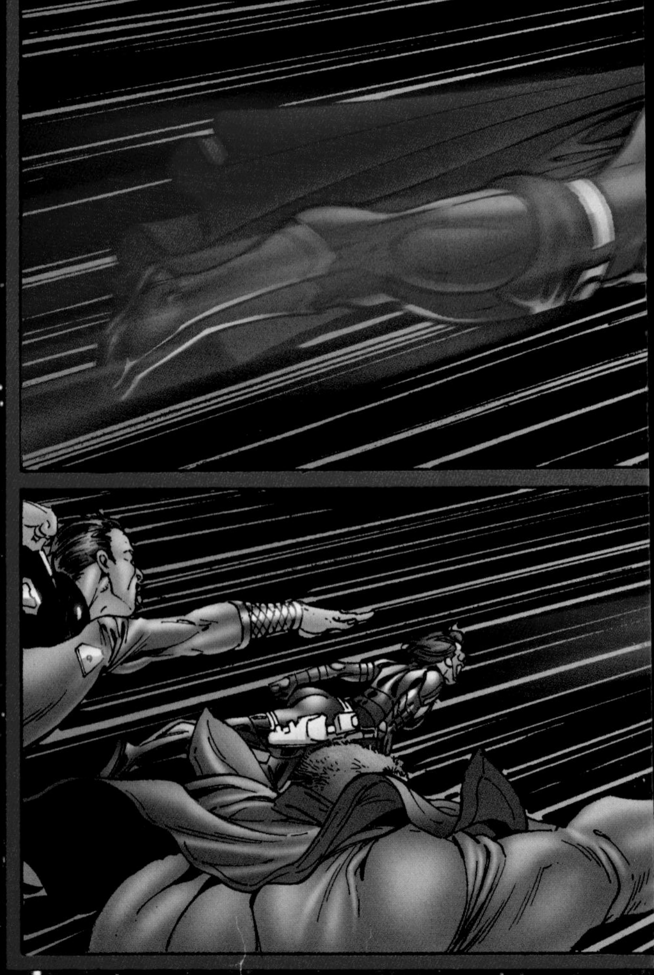

THERE'S ALWAYS HOPE!

ZOR-EL'S TOMB.
ONE MILE UNDERNEATH.
N-NO... STOP! PLEASE!

AAAAAH!

ARE YOU LISTENING NOW, REACTRON? YOU HAVE INFORMATION ABOUT THE PEOPLE OF EARTH WHO ARE PLOTTING AGAINST US.
WE KNOW THEY ARE. ONE OF THEM WAS EVEN WORKING WITH BRAINIAC.

"YOU'RE GOING TO TELL ME EVERYTHING YOU KNOW ABOUT THESE MEN, OR I'M GOING TO TURN THE KVORN BACK ON..."

...AND THEN I'LL TURN IT UP TO MAXIMUM.
"WATCH OUT FOR YOUR MOTHER."

THAT'S WHAT FATHER SAID TO ME AS HE DIED.
"WATCH OUT FOR YOUR MOTHER."
UH-OHHH... BUSTEEED...

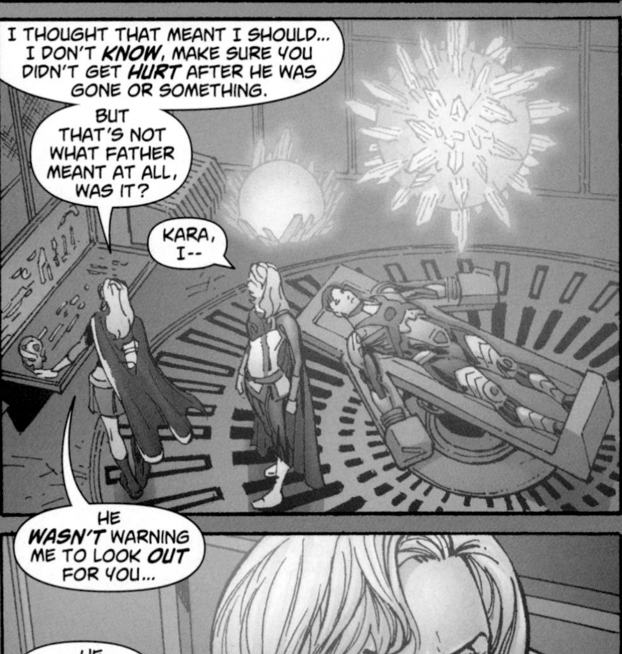
I THOUGHT THAT MEANT I SHOULD... I DON'T KNOW, MAKE SURE YOU DIDN'T GET HURT AFTER HE WAS GONE OR SOMETHING.
BUT THAT'S NOT WHAT FATHER MEANT AT ALL, WAS IT?
KARA, I--

HE WASN'T WARNING ME TO LOOK OUT FOR YOU...
...HE WAS WARNING ME ABOUT YOU.

"DON'T YOU DARE JUDGE ME, KARA."

REACTRON IS A PRISONER OF THE STATE, AND HE HAS INFORMATION NECESSARY FOR THE PROTECTION OF OUR PEOPLE--
"OUR PEOPLE"? HAVE YOU LOST YOUR FREAKING MIND?
YOU'RE BEEN TORTURING SOMEONE DOWN HERE, MOM! SOMEONE YOU SENT ME TO EARTH TO BRING BACK TO NEW KRYPTON.
THAT MAKES ME RESPONSIBLE FOR HIM. JUST AS IT MAKES ME COMPLICIT IN A WAR CRIME.

IF I HAVE TO GO TO EXTREME MEASURES TO GET INFORMATION OUT OF HIM--
--INFORMATION THAT WILL KEEP OUR PLANET SAFE--

--IT'S WORTH IT.

"THAT'S HOW YOU JUSTIFY THIS?"
YOU THINK THE SAFETY OF NEW KRYPTON IS SO IMPORTANT WE HAVE TO BEAT INFORMATION OUT OF SOMEONE--
HOW NAÏVE CAN YOU BE, KARA?
OR HAVE YOU FORGOTTEN THAT THIS... MONSTER... MURDERED YOUR FATHER IN OUR STREETS--
I KNOW HE DID, MOM. I WAS THERE.
DAD DIED SAVING MY LIFE.
IN FACT, WHERE WERE YOU WHEN HE DIED?
HEH HH HEH...
...WHAT'S SO FUNNY?
YOU TWO... ARGUING ABOUT WHAT MOM'S BEEN DOING...
...LEMME TELL YOU SOMETHING THAT'S JUST GONNA... BLOW YOU AWAY...

"...WE WANTED YOU TO BRING ME HERE..."

DADEET
DADEET
WHAT?
WE HAD YOU DEAD TO RIGHTS IN LOS ANGELES, SUPERCHEEKS... BUT WE DIDN'T TAKE THE KILL SHOT... JUST SET YOU FREE SO YOU COULD FIND ME AGAIN...
...AMAZING... YOU DIDN'T THINK TO ASK WHY...

OKAY. FINE.
WHY?
KARA, SOMETHING'S WRONG...
...YOU K'S ALL LEFT EARTH SO QUICKLY... WE DIDN'T HAVE TIME TO PROPERLY SAY GOODBYE...
...AN' WHILE ALL YOU KRYPTONIANS... WERE OFF FIGHTIN' BRAINIAC...

...LANE'S ERRAND BOY, LUTHOR, SLIPPED IN HERE AND LEFT ME WITH A LITTLE PRESENT FOR YOU...
...HH... FEELS LIKE IT JUST KICKED ON...

...A PARTING GIFT... FROM THE EARTH TO YOU...

"...BEEN TICKING THIS WHOLE TIME... INSIDE ME..."

KARA, INSIDE THE RADIATION DECK, NOW!
...THINK THE COUNTDOWN'S ALMOST UP...
...SO YOU AND MOM CAN ARGUE ABOUT MORALS AND VALUES ALL YOU WANT...

WAIT! WHAT ARE YOU--
YOU'LL BE SAFE IN HERE. I'M GOING TO TRY TO STOP THIS.
MOM!
VZZZT

...BUT YOU'RE BOTH ABOUT TO MEET UP WITH DADDY EL...
...HH...GLAD I GOT TO COMPLETE... THE WHOLE FAMILY SET...

MOM!
MOM!

"UNIMAGINABLE..."

EARTH.
METROPOLIS.
...WHAT MY FATHER'S OPERATION HAS BEEN DOING. WHAT THEY'VE BEEN PLANNING.
PROJECT 7734 IS RESPONSIBLE FOR A NUMBER OF ATROCITIES, THE LEAST OF WHICH WAS TURNING MY SISTER INTO SUPERWOMAN.
BUT NOW, WITH ALL OF THE PIECES OF THE PUZZLE IN FRONT OF US, WE'VE FIGURED OUT THEIR ENDGAME.
GENERAL LANE'S PLANNING TO DESTROY NEW KRYPTON. AND IT COULD HAPPEN AT ANY MOMENT.
HOW DO YOU KNOW?
SOMEONE FEEDING US INTEL FROM THE INSIDE. SOME OF YOU KNOW HER.
'CEPT MAYBE YOU AND FLAMEBIRD, NIGHTWING.
NATASHA IRONS.
SHE RELAYED TO ME THAT SHE'D GOTTEN THE PROOF THAT WILL FINALLY TAKE LANE DOWN.
SHE WAS SUPPOSED TO DELIVER IT TO ME TWO DAYS AGO. SHE NEVER SHOWED.
WE CAN ONLY ASSUME GENERAL LANE'S GOTTEN HER. IF THAT'S TRUE--
YEAH, JIMMY--

SO LANE'S TRYING TO WIPE OUT THE KRYPTONIANS?
I KNEW THAT MONSTER COULDN'T BE TRUSTED.

BUT IF GENERAL LANE HAD LAUNCHED SOME KIND OF WEAPON, WE'D KNOW ABOUT IT, RIGHT? SOMEONE WOULD'VE SEEN IT.
THE JUSTICE LEAGUE SATELLITE WOULD'VE PICKED IT UP--
NOT NECESSARILY.
FEW YEARS AGO, THERE WAS A LOT OF CHATTER ABOUT THE U.S. GOVERNMENT HAVING ACCESS TO BOOM TUBE TELEPORTATION TECHNOLOGY.
HELL, I'VE EVEN HEARD THAT THE GOVERNMENT HAS SOMETHING CALLED A "TIME POOL"--
IT DOESN'T MATTER HOW THEY'RE GOING TO DO IT.
MY DAD'S GOT THE WHOLE WORLD THINKING HE HAS HUMANITY'S BEST INTERESTS AT HEART.
WE KNOW HE'S LYING.
IT'S UP TO US TO GET NATASHA IRONS BACK AND FIND OUT WHAT SHE UNCOVERED--
--AND EXPOSE MY FATHER FOR THE MANIAC THAT HE IS.

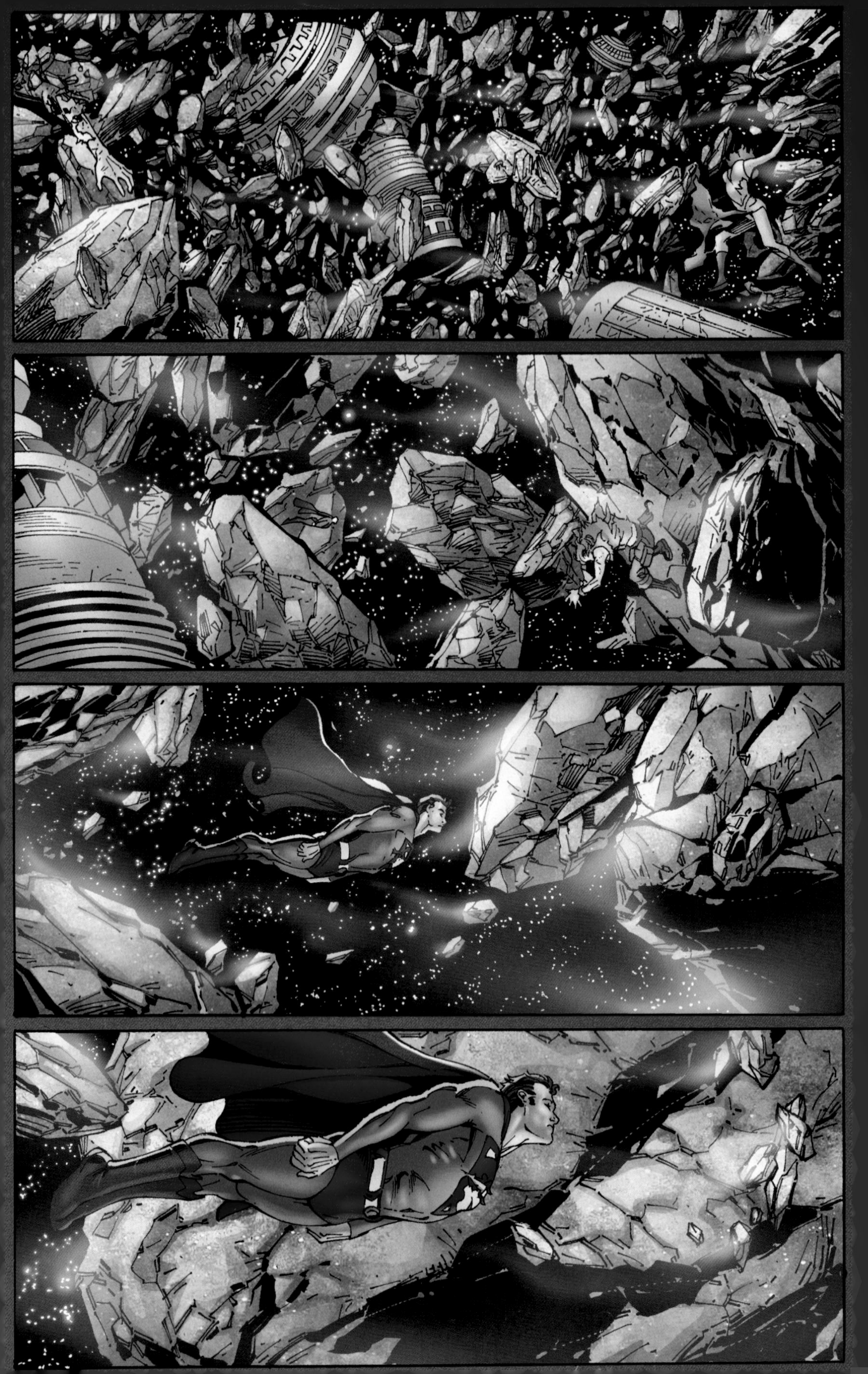

"...LANE'S ERRAND BOY, LUTHOR, SLIPPED IN HERE AND LEFT ME WITH A LITTLE PRESENT FOR YOU...
"...HH...FEELS LIKE IT JUST KICKED ON..."
...A PARTING GIFT... FROM THE EARTH TO YOU...

THE NEW KRYPTONIAN ARMADA. 97 MILLION KILOMETERS FROM EARTH.
AND CLOSING.
I AM SO PROUD.
I AM SO PROUD.
MY MEN. MY ARMY.
I APPEAR...ADDRESS MY FORCES AND STATE PLAINLY THAT THEIR WORLD IS NO MORE.
THEIR LOVED ONES, THE LIFE THEY HAD...
...DESTROYED FOREVER.
THEY REACT, OF COURSE. SOME CRY. SOME COLLAPSE, WAILING, ENVELOPED IN THEIR GRIEF. IT'S TO BE EXPECTED, AND I THINK NO WORSE OF THOSE WHO DO.

BUT THE MAJORITY STAND FIRM.
HURTING. HEARTBROKEN. OF COURSE.
BUT RESOLVED.
OH, MY ARMY...
...I AM SO PROUD.
YES, MY SOLDIERS, OUR PLANET IS LOST.
AND I AM CERTAIN THAT EVEN AS I SPEAK OUR ENEMY PROCLAIMS ITS VICTORY OVER US.
BUT EARTH CANNOT CONCEIVE THE STRENGTH OF OUR WILL.
NEW KRYPTON...WE, THE LAST OF OUR RACE.
THE WAR GOES ON...
...AND WE WILL WIN IT.

METROPOLIS.
PERRY!
I NEED PRODUCTION TO HOLD THE PLATE, AND I NEED THIS ONLINE ASAP!
WE JUST GOT WORD FROM MY GUY AT NASA! NEW KRYPTON'S GONE!
LOIS, SLOW DOWN! WHAT'S HAPPENED TO NEW KRYPTON?
HE DID IT, PERRY. HE DESTROYED IT.
LIKE I KNEW HE WOULD.
ALL RIGHT, YOU HEARD HER! WE'VE GOT A PLANET IN PIECES, PEOPLE!
I WANT CITIZENS' REACTIONS, EXPERT OPINIONS, THE WORKS! HOW DOES THIS AFFECT US? WHAT HAPPENED TO THE KRYPTONIANS? GET ON IT!
YOU OKAY?
I'LL BE FINE.
WHO DESTROYED NEW KRYPTON, LOIS? AND HOW IS THAT EVEN POSSIBLE?
ONE MAN KNEW HOW TO DO IT, PERRY. HE'S BEEN PLANNING THIS. THE MANIAC WHO WANTED ALL OF THE KRYPTONIANS DEAD.
MY FATHER.
THE "ILLUSTRIOUS" GENERAL SAM LA--

KRRKKSHHH

NN
KAFF KAFF
SUPERWOMAN?
YOU'RE NOT EVEN WORTHY TO SAY DADDY'S NAME, LOIS.
L-LUCY?
LOIS?
LOIS!
LOIS!
PERRY, WHAT ARE WE GOING TO DO? AND IF NEW KRYPTON'S GONE...
...DOES THAT MEAN SUPERMAN IS, TOO?

KRNCH!

CALLISTO, MOON OF NEW KRYPTON.
DEEP BELOW THE SURFACE.
THERE. WE SHOULD HAVE ENOUGH ATMOSPHERE DOWN HERE SO WE CAN TALK.
KARA, WHAT HAPPENED--

NNYAH!

AAH!

STOP.
KRAK

I KNOW YOU'RE UPSET, KARA, BUT YOU NEED TO TELL ME WHAT HAPPENED.

IT WAS ME, KAL! ALL BECAUSE OF ME.
I DESTROYED NEW KRYPTON.

WHAT?

--AND REACTRON THANKED ME FOR BRINGING HIM BACK TO NEW KRYPTON. SAID IT WAS ALL PART OF THE PLAN.
THEN HE STARTED TO GLOW.
MOM THREW ME INTO THAT CHAMBER... AND THEN REACTRON--
--HE--
KAL, I--I WAS RESPONSIBLE FOR REACTRON BEING THERE. IS ALL OF THIS MY FAULT?
DID I KILL OUR... OUR P-PEOPLE? COULD I HAVE SAVED THEM?
YOU DIDN'T KILL ANYONE, KARA. REACTRON WAS ONE OF LANE'S MEN.
THAT MEANS THAT LANE'S PLAYED ALL OF US. EVEN BRAINIAC.
YOU COULDN'T HAVE KNOWN HIS PLANS, OR HOW FAR HE WOULD GO.
OH, GOD, KAL! WHAT IF THERE ARE SURVIVORS?
WE HAVE TO GO BACK AND--AND LOOK--
I'M... I'M SORRY, KARA. I LOOKED EVERYWHERE.
YOU WERE THE ONLY SURVIVOR.
I LOVE YOU, KARA.
I LOVE YOU TOO, KAL...
...I--I JUST CAN'T BELIEVE THEY'RE ALL GONE.

I KNOW THIS IS HARD TO HEAR RIGHT NOW, KARA, BUT ZOD'S DECLARED WAR ON EARTH--
WHAT?
--AND HE'S NOT GOING TO STOP HIS CHARGE UNTIL THE EARTH IS IN ASHES. ESPECIALLY NOT AFTER THIS.
KAL, I CAN'T FIGHT OUR PEOPLE, NOT AFTER--
KARA, YOUR MOTHER GAVE HER LIFE TO SAVE YOURS.
WE'RE THE ONLY PEOPLE WHO CAN KEEP THIS CONFLICT FROM GOING ANY FURTHER...
...OR ELSE ANOTHER RACE WILL DIE TODAY.
OKAY.
OKAY, YOU'RE RIGHT.
WHAT DO WE DO NOW?

"HOW LONG HAS IT BEEN, URSA?"
SINCE WHEN, GENERAL?
NEW KRYPTON... OUR PLANET... SINCE...
HOW LONG?
44 DENDARO.
IN EARTH TIME.
I WANT TO KNOW IN A WAY GENERAL LANE WILL UNDERSTAND WHEN I TELL HIM HOW MUCH TIME PASSED BETWEEN THE MOMENT OF NEW KRYPTON'S DESTRUCTION AND HIS OWN.
RIGHT BEFORE I RIP THE HEAD FROM HIS SHOULDERS.
27 MINUTES.
I FAILED THEM, URSA. OUR PEOPLE.
THEN AVENGE THEM. WE CAN DO THAT AT LEAST.
YES. ONWARD.

EARTH.
NIGHTWING?
...I SEE HER, FLAMEBIRD. NATASHA IRONS IS IN THERE.
HER CELL'S... DARK...THERE ARE LOTS OF SHADOWS FOR ME TO PEER THROUGH...
...SHE'S SLEEPING... I SMELL...DUST AND BLOOD AND SWEAT... AND PAIN...
PAIN?
IF THE HUMAN DEFENSE CORPS HAS HURT HER, I'M GONNA FIND GENERAL LANE AND KICK HIS--
EASY, JIMMY. WE'LL GET MY NIECE OUT OF THERE. SHE'S BEEN IN WORSE SCRAPES BEFORE.
FUNNY PLACE FOR A SECRET GOVERNMENT BASE, DON'T YOU THINK?
NAH.
I KNEW SOME GUYS WHO USED TO HANG OUT HERE. ON THE INSIDE, IT'S ACTUALLY A PRETTY SECURE LOCATION.

ON THE *OUTSIDE*, IT'S A PRETTY COOL SCULPTURE.
SO, C'MON.
LET'S GO SMASH IT UP.

GENERAL LANE, SIR. MAY I ASK YOU A QUESTION?
OF COURSE, DREW. SPEAK.
OBVIOUSLY, WITH THE CODENAME "ASSASSIN," I'VE KILLED MORE PEOPLE THAN I CAN RECALL.
AND?
IT'S JUST, I WAS WONDERING... WHAT DOES IT FEEL LIKE TO KILL A PLANET?
A PLANET OF ALIENS, DREW, THAT'S WHAT'S IMPORTANT. AND IN RESPONSE, HONESTLY...
I DON'T THINK I'VE EVER BEEN HAPPIER IN MY LIFE.
GENERAL.
AH, MY DAUGHTER.
MISSION ACCOMPLISHED, SIR.
WITH MY OTHER DAUGHTER. HELLO, LOIS.
DAD!
WE'VE GOT SOME CATCHING UP TO DO. LOTS TO TALK ABOUT.
TELL ME, THEN. WHY WAS I TAKEN? WHAT'S GOING ON?
LET'S JUST SAY...
...DADDY'S BEEN BUSY.

HUMAN DEFENSE CORPS, MARS BASE.
RED ALERT! RED ALERT!
FULL MOBILIZATION!

EVERYTHING IN PLACE?
EVERYTHING IS PERFECT.

COME ON, LADIES, LET'S GET THESE BIRDS FLYING! WE'RE EARTH'S FIRST LINE OF DEFENSE, AIN'T WE?...

COME ON, COME ON, LET'S GET THEM IN THE AIR!

ALL HANDS!
LAUNCH THE FLEET! GET THE DAMN FLEET IN THE AIR!
ALL HANDS!
RED ALERT! KRYPTONIAN SHIPS PASSING EARTHWARD IN FIVE AND COUNTING!
...TIME TO EARN OUR PAY!
I HEAR THAT.
OUR MEN ARE READY?
AND UNDER WAY.
hhh
GENERAL?
THE IRONY. ONE OF THE THINGS I HAD KAL-EL TEACH OUR TROOPS WITHOUT HIS EVER KNOWING WHY I REALLY WANTED IT...
PRECISION LOW-LEVEL FLYING.
YES. IN THIS CASE...

"...UNDER THE RADAR OF EARTH'S MARS BASE."

"GENERAL..."
...THE HUMAN DEFENSE CORPS SPACE FLEET...OUR FLEET...
...DESTROYED.
GENERAL...
GENERAL...

"...IT'S KAL-EL AND HIS COUSIN!"
"IT'S SUPERMAN AND SUPERGIRL!"

YES...
...OF COURSE IT IS.
WHAT DO WE DO NOW?
"ANYTHING... EVERYTHING WE CAN TO DEFUSE THIS INSANITY UNTIL WE CAN ARRIVE AT AN ANSWER.
"ANYTHING WE CAN DO TO SAVE LIVES...
"...ON BOTH SIDES."
USE THAT FACT... THAT KAL-EL'S NOT ON EARTH.
SECOND WAVE ALREADY DEPLOYED, AS PER YOUR COMMAND, GENERAL!
EARTH IT IS!
GENERAL LANE...

..A LARGE BODY OF
RYPTONIANS IS NOW
VEERING TOWARDS
EARTH."
LUTHOR? PROGRESS?
SOON.
THEY'LL BE ENTERING OUR ATMOSPHERE IN A MINUTE AND THREE, GENERAL. A MINUTE AND TWO. ONE. SIXTY SECONDS. FIFTY-N--
IF YOU WANT YOUR SIDE OF OUR AGREEMENT, LUTHOR... NO, IF YOU WANT TO LIVE...
"--IGHT, FORTY-SEVEN, FORTY-SIX, FORTY-FI--"
NOW, LUTHOR!
ALL RIGHT. ALL RIGHT. NO NEED TO SHOUT.

"...'SOON' HAD BETTER BE NOW."
I'M CREATING A WEAPON THAT COMBINES THE CADAVER OF A KRYPTONIAN "GOD" WITH TIME-POOL TECHNOLOGY...
...IT TAKES AS LONG AS IT TAKES.
THANK YOU. YOU ARE ONCE AGAIN THE OWNER OF LEXCORP.
NO, THANK YOU, GENERAL.
"AND YOU ARE NOW THE OWNER...

"...OF A BIG RED SUN."

EDDY BARROWS + JP MAYER
ROD REIS

LOPRESTI '10
RYAN
BA

PROJECT 7734.
--CONFIRMED! THE SUN HAS GONE RED! ALL K'S ARE POWERLESS--
--RECONFIGURING SATELLITES TO GET IMAGERY--
--HAVE IT IN THREE, TWO, ONE--
GENERAL, WE GOT VISUALS COMING IN FROM MARS BASE.
ON THE MAIN SCREEN, PLEASE.
NO!
HOLD STILL, YOU STUPID COW--
DON'T CALL YOUR SISTER NAMES, LUCY.
LT. HOLLISTER, GET ME THE PRESIDENT. HUMANKIND JUST WON THE WAR WITH THE KRYPTONIANS...
...AND HE HAS ME TO THANK.
SIR? WE'VE JUST GOTTEN WORD FROM MT. RUSHMORE. OUR FORCES THERE HAVE BEEN CRUSHED.
THE KRYPTONIANS? HOW? THEY--
NO, SIR, NOT THE KRYPTONIANS...

"...SOMEONE ELSE."
MT. RUSHMORE
--THINK THE FOUNDING FATHERS WOULD BE VERY DISAPPOINTED IN YOU JERKS!

THOOOM
YOU OKAY, KID?
YEAH, BETTER THAN THOSE HUMAN DEFENSE CORPS GUYS.
LOOKS LIKE WE FOUND OUR GIRL. WE READY TO GO?
NOT YET.
WHAT'S THAT, JIM?
SOMETHING STEEL COOKED UP ON THE FLIGHT OVER. IT'S CONVERTING THE INFORMATION IN NATASHA'S HEAD INTO ORGANIZED DIGITAL STREAMING DATA.
KINDA TINGLES, OLSEN.
SORRY.
MY CONTACTS HAVE HACKED EVERY MAJOR NEWS OUTLET ON THE INTERNET. SOON AS I SEND THIS, WE'RE GOING TO BROADCAST WHAT WE'VE GOT AGAINST LANE.
YOU--NNN--HAVE A LOT OF FRIENDS ON THE INTERNET?
OF COURSE, MR. HARPER. THERE ARE PEOPLE LIKE ME EVERYWHERE.
MY NEWSGROUP EVEN HAS A CODENAME.
WE CALL OURSELVES "THE NEWSBOY LEGION."
COGNITIVE DATA DOWNLOAD COMPLETE.
SEND
KDEET

AAAH!
FLAMEBIRD?!
L--LUTHOR--
--USED THE CORPSE OF THE FALSE-RAO--
--CORRUPTED IT WITH HIS SCIENCE AND USED IT TO CHANGE THE SUN--
--KARA--
--KAL-EL--
--SOMEONE'S USING OUR GOD TO MURDER OUR PEOPLE--
--OUR FRIENDS... OUR--OUR FAMILIES!
STAY HERE, NIGHTWING!
THE KRYPTONIANS MUST LIVE!

SUPERBOY! I'M-I'M SORRY. I HAVE TO GO.
WHAT?! WE'RE IN THE MIDDLE OF A FIGHT HERE! WE NEED YOU GUYS!
THE FLAMEBIRD NEEDS ME MORE.
TELL...TELL SUPERMAN I'M SORRY I DIDN'T GET TO SEE HIM AGAIN.
WHAT? NIGHTWING!
NIGHTWING!
NIGHTWING. I TOLD YOU TO STAY --
THE TWO OF US MUST STOP THE FALSE-RAO, FLAMEBIRD. WE PLAYED A PART IN HIS CREATION.
THE ENERGIES REQUIRED TO EXPUNGE FALSE-RAO FROM THIS SUN ARE UNQUANTIFIABLE.
THIS ACTION COULD PROVE FATAL TO OUR HOST BODIES.
I WOULD NEVER LET YOU DO THIS ALONE, THARA.
THAT'S NOT WHAT LOVERS DO.

WHAT ARE THOSE TWO STREAKS, LIEUTENANT?
ENERGY SIGNATURES MATCH KNOWN META-KRYPTONIAN COMBATANTS "NIGHTWING" AND "FLAMEBIRD," SIR.
AH. THE KRYPTONIANS' LAST STAND.
CHRIS...
THEIR SCIENCE CORRUPTS RAO'S BODY.
THIS IS... IT'S SO HOT IN HERE...THARA, WHAT DO WE DO NOW?
YOU'LL DO NOTHING, CHRIS KENT.
WHAT? THE NIGHTWING--
YOUR FINAL FATE LIES ELSEWHERE--
--UNLIKE THARA AK-VAR'S.
WHAT? NO! WAIT!
THARA!
DO NOT WORRY, CHRIS. SHE KNOWS OF YOUR LOVE...
I'M SORRY, CHRIS. IT HAS TO BE THIS WAY.
THARA!
...AND THAT THOUGHT WILL COMFORT HER...
...IN THE END.

NNNN... NOT... ENOUGH...
...ONE MORE...
AAAAAAAHH!

WE'RE GETTING ZERO RESPONSE FROM LUTHOR'S TECH, SIR... WHATEVER NIGHTWING AND FLAMEBIRD DID IN THERE...
WILL SOMEONE PLEASE TELL ME WHAT JUST HAPPENED?!
"...IT WORKED."

"SEVEN THOUSAND, URSA..."

...THAT'S ALL THAT REMAINS OF OUR PEOPLE.
RAO. TWO HOURS AGO THERE WERE EIGHTY THOUSAND.
YOU'RE NOT SUGGESTING THAT WE'VE LOST, GENERAL.
OF COURSE I'M NOT.
COME...

REMIND EARTH WHO WE ARE."
--NEWS COMING IN--
--REPORTS ALL OVER THE WORLD--
DESTRUCTION ACROSS THE--
--WAVE OF ATTACKS IN THE LAST--
OH MY GOD! NO! WE'RE GETTING WORD--
--REPORT. HORRI--
--BRITISH PRIME MINISTER IS DEAD--
--DOWNING STREET IS RUBBLE, MANY THOUSANDS

--IME MINISTER OF JAPAN TORN APART--
--FRENCH PRESIDENT ALSO--
HEROES OF EARTH--
--SOME OF THEM--
--RESISTING--

--TONIANS TOO STRONG FOR--
--STRIKES HAPPENING TOO QUI--
--SURGICAL STRIKES ON--
--TTACKING HUMAN DEFENSE CORPS BASES AROUND THE WORLD.
--ANTARCTICA--
--COUNTER SURGE AT THE AUSTRALIAN BASE--
--GREEN KRYPTONITE--
--ROBOT ARMY-- APPARENTLY BUILT BY DR. WILL MAG--
--G.I. ROBOT LEADING THE--

OTHER LOCATIONS--
--H.D.C. FORCES MANAGING TO OUTFIGHT--
--CALL OUT TO THE SUPER-TEAMS OF AMERICA--
--MANY OF WHOM HAVE YET TO--
--OTHER HEROES FAILING TO REPEL--
--DEFEATED--
--ATTACKS HAPPENING TOO FAST!

--THE ATTACKS NOW--
--KRYPTONIAN ASSAULTS--
--TOO MANY--
--TOO FAST--
--THOUSANDS DYING FOR EVERY ONE KRYPTONIAN--
--HEROES OF THE WORLD CAN'T REACT--
--GLOBAL GUARDIANS ARE--
--ATTACKS AT KEY SITES ALL OVER THE PLANET.
--KRYPTONIAN IDENTIFIED--
URSA, A LEADING MEMBER OF GENERAL ZOD'S--
--TRAJECTORY OF ATTACKS--
ESTIMATES--
THE WHITE HOUSE.

--DESTROYED.
--ND WE'RE TRYING TO ASCERTAIN IF THE PRESIDENT HAS BEEN--
HE CAN'T HIDE FROM ME. EVEN IF I HAVE TO TEAR THIS WORLD APART, I WILL FIND HIM.
NO, URSA. YOU WON'T--
--NOW THAT I'VE FOUND YOU.

--REPORTS OF A MASSIVE GROUP OF KRYPTONIANS--

--WAIT! WAIT! ZOD'S BEEN SIGHTED--
GENERAL ZOD IS LEADING THEM--
--CONFIRMED--
--BASED ON OUR INFORMATION--
--DIRECTIONAL HEADING OF THIS LARGE PARTY--
--METROPOLIS.
WAIT! HOLD ON!
--WE'VE JUST BEEN TOLD THAT NONE OF THE CITY'S HEROES ARE CURRENTLY THERE.
WHERE STEEL, MON-EL AND THE GUARDIAN ARE--
--WHY THEY'RE GONE IS A MYSTERY--
--THE QUESTION NOW...

...WHO WILL SAVE METROPOLIS?

PART 4: THE BATTLE FOR SURVIVAL Cover by EDDY BARROWS, J.P. MAYER & ROD REIS

RYAN

THE OVAL OFFICE. WASHINGTON, D.C.
HIGH OVER THE UNITED STATES.
SEVEN KLICKS THAT WAY, UNCLE JOHN.
WHEN I WAS WORKING UNDERCOVER FOR GENERAL LANE, I FOUND OUT WHERE ALL OF HIS HIDDEN BASES ARE.
PROJECT 7734, BUNKER 13. FAR BELOW THE PENTAGON.
WHAT DO WE DO WITH THE KRYPTONIAN PRISONERS, SIR?
MY ORDERS WERE CLEAR, LIEUTENANT.
THIS IS WAR. WE TAKE NO PRISONERS.
CAIRO.
YOU HEARD HIM, MEN.
FZP
THIS ENDS NOW, ZOD.

METROPOLIS.
I DON'T **THINK** SO, KAL-EL.
THESE **HUMANS** HAVE DRIVEN US RIGHT TO THE **BRINK** OF EXTINCTION, AND ALL YOU CAN THINK ABOUT IS **PROTECTING** THEM.
KRAK
WHAT ABOUT PROTECTING **OUR** PEOPLE? MAKING SURE **WE** SURVIVE?
HUMANKIND **MURDERED** MOST OF OUR RACE TODAY, SO I'M HERE FOR ONE SIMPLE REASON...

EVENGE.
HOLD
IM THERE,
MEN.
NO! WHY-- WHY AREN'T ANY OF YOU LISTENING TO ME?
THIS WAR IS JUST GOING TO UP THE CASUALTIES ON BOTH SIDES--
I UNDERSTAND YOU'RE ALL HURTING RIGHT NOW, BUT THAT DOESN'T MEAN THAT ALL OF HUMANKIND SHOULD SUFFER, TOO--
OH, I DISAGREE, "SUPERMAN."
EVERYONE ON THIS PLANET DESERVES TO SUFFER. AND THEY WILL.

KA-CHOOOOM
NOW, FIND ME LOIS LA--
ZOD!
"YOU STUPID LITTLE FOOL!"

THEY DESTROYED YOUR PLANET! THEY MURDERED KRYPTON!
HOW CAN YOU DEFEND THEM?
I KNOW THE GUILTY WILL BE PUNISHED, URSA!
YES. BY ME!
AND YOU? GUILTY OF STUPIDITY AND TREASON AGAINST YOUR RACE.
HERE'S YOUR PUNISHMENT...
...A TRAITOR'S DE--

-AAAAAAAHH!
GGRRRR
NORMALLY I HAVE A RULE ABOUT HITTING WOMEN, BUT WITH YOU I'LL MAKE AN **EXCEPTION**.
THE WHITE HOUSE. THEY DESTROYED THE DAMN WHITE HOUSE.
KARA? YOU OKAY?
NICK OF TIME, CONNER. HOW DID YOU KNOW--?
ME AND THE GUYS WERE ON OUR WAY TO GENERAL LANE'S BASE WHEN WE SAW YOU.
OKAY, THOSE SYNTHETIC GOLD KRYPTONITE CUFFS WILL HOLD HER... I THINK. BUT WHAT DO WE **DO** WITH HER?
NIGHTWING SAID THE PHANTOM ZONE WAS BACK BEFORE HE DISAPPEARED, RIGHT?
I NEED YOU TO FETCH ME SOMETHING, BOY.
"YOU'RE NOT DESTROYING EARTH, ZOD..."

...I WON'T LET YOU!
OH, I'LL LET THE PLANET SURVIVE, EL...IT'S JUST ITS PEOPLE I'M GOING TO ERADICATE!
MY SOLDIERS-- THE LAST SURVIVING KRYPTONIANS--WILL NEED A NEW WORLD, AND WHAT BETTER PLACE THAN THIS ONE.
I KNOW YOU'RE ANGRY ABOUT WHAT HAPPENED TO NEW KRYPTON. SO AM I. BUT--
"BUT MY ANGER AT THE HOUSE OF EL IS BOUNDLESS."

"NO, EL..."
...YOU'VE NEVER UNDER-STOOD ME. YOU OR YOUR FATHER.
YES, I'M ANGRY. AT LANE. AT EARTH.
EVEN IF YOU BEAT ME, THE JUSTICE LEAGUE IS STILL OUT THERE--
THE JUSTICE LEAGUE? HA...
SHHINNNG

"...WHERE DO YOU THINK I'VE SENT NON?"
KRAK
HAHA HAHAHA!
HEY, NON, BUDDY! OVER HERE!

SMILE FOR THE CAMERA!
OOPS, MY MISTAKE--THIS IS A PHANTOM ZONE PROJECTOR!
TELL URSA I SAID "HI."
HRAAAAHHHHHHH--!
GOOD DOG.
HRRF
"CAN YOU SEE IT?"

WE'VE GOT REPORTS COMING IN FROM ALL OVER THE GLOBE! MY MEN ARE SUCCESSFULLY STOPPING THESE K'S FROM--
FROM WHAT, DAD? STAYING ALIVE? YOU'RE KILLING PRISONERS AND COMBATANTS ALIKE NOW.
OF COURSE WE'RE KILLING THEM, LOIS.
THE KRYPTONIANS ARE RABID DOGS WHO NEED TO BE PUT DOWN BEFORE--
SPOKEN LIKE A TRUE GENOCIDAL MANIAC.
"MANIAC"? YOU MEAN VISIONARY!
I BROUGHT YOU HERE SO I COULD SHOW YOU HOW I'M KEEPING THIS PLANET SAFE, LOIS.
I KNEW FROM THE MOMENT SUPERMAN SET FOOT ON THIS WORLD, HE WAS GOING TO LEAD TO ITS DESTRUCTION. HOW ONE ALIEN WOULD BE THE DEATH OF MILLIONS--
YOU JUST DESTROYED AN ENTIRE PLANET! DON'T YOU SEE THAT, TO THE KRYPTONIANS, YOU'RE THAT "ONE ALIEN"?
WHAT? NO... I...
SIR!
WE HAVE INTRUDERS! SUPERGIRL AND OTHER NON-K'S!
SUPERWOMAN AND OUR "OTHERS" HAVE ENGAGED THEM, I HOPE.
YES, SIR, BUT--
THEN WE'LL BE FINE.
THAT'S WHAT I'M TRYING TO TELL YOU, SIR...
"...SUPERWOMAN IS ALREADY DOWN."

YOU KILLED MY FATHER.
THAT WHAT YOU CALL HIM, CLONE? I'M CODENAME: ASSASSIN. I DID MY JOB.
YOU LIKE IT, THOUGH, HUH? I CAN SEE THAT. "ASSASSIN"? PSYCHO!
YOU MURDERED THE ORIGINAL JIM HARPER, AND I HAD TO WATCH!
YOU...FOR THAT...YOU DESERVE--
SUPERGIRL! YOU OKAY OVER THERE?
YEAH, I'M JUST...LISTENING FOR...
--START EVAC, LT. HOLLISTER. MY DAUGHTER AND I WILL TAKE THE SHUTTLE--
THERE.
"JOR-EL DIDN'T UNDERSTAND, EL..."

...HE LOOKED ME IN THE EYE, AND STILL HE SENT NON, URSA AND ME INTO THE HELL THAT IS THE PHANTOM ZONE.
I SWORE TO YOUR FATHER THAT DAY...
...VOWED THAT HIS HEIRS WOULD SUFFER FOR HIS SINS.
"SUPERGIRL, STOP!"
THIS ISN'T JUSTICE--
THIS MAN MURDERED MY RACE TODAY, LOIS.
HKKL
THIS IS AS CLOSE TO JUSTICE AS HE DESERVES.
SEE... LOIS?
...RABID... DOGS...
SHUT UP!
"I CAN'T TELL YOU WHAT PLEASURE IT'S GOING TO GIVE ME..."
...CUTTING THE HEART FROM YOUR CHEST, THEN TAKING THIS WORLD AS OUR OWN--
NEW NEW KRYPTON?

NAH, THAT JUST DOESN'T HAVE QUITE THE SAME RING TO IT.
THE PHANTOM ZONE PROJECTOR? BUT THE ZONE'S GONE!
I DESTROYED IT--
WHAT CAN I SAY? IT GOT BETTER.
IT'S A SHAME YOU WON'T.
HRRK
KRYPTO!
"PLEASE! DON'T KILL HIM!"

KARA, I KNOW YOU'RE HURTING. YES, MY FATHER IS A MURDERER. BUT YOU'RE NOT.
DON'T LET HIM CHANGE THAT. DON'T LET HIM CHANGE YOU.
PLEASE, SUPERGIRL...
...LET GO.
HHHHHHHHH
SO WHAT HAPPENS NOW?
WE TELL THE WORLD WHAT HAPPENED. MY FATHER FACES AN INTERNATIONAL COURT FOR THE CRIMES HE'S COMMITTED--
I... DON'T THINK SO...
I SAID NO PRISONERS, LOIS...
...AND I MEANT IT.
NO!
"HOW DOES IT FEEL, SUPERBOY--"

--KNOWING THE DOG SACRIFICED ITSELF FOR NOTHI--
SUPERMAN!
KNNCH
GET KRYPTO INTO DIRECT SUNLIGHT, SUPERBOY. HE'LL BE FINE.
WHICH IS MORE THAN I CAN SAY FOR THE GENERAL HERE.
EVEN IF YOU PUT ME BACK IN THE ZONE, KAL-EL, I'LL FIND A WAY BACK OUT--
I KNOW, ZOD. YOU'VE PROVEN TO ME THAT YOU'RE THE MAN I ALWAYS THOUGHT YOU WERE. TREACHEROUS. DANGEROUS.
I'VE SET THE PROJECTOR TO SELF-DESTRUCT AS SOON AS WE'RE BOTH INSIDE. I'M SEALING THE ZONE COMPLETELY.
YOU'LL BE BACK IN YOUR PRISON FOREVER, ZOD--
I'LL WILLINGLY SACRIFICE MYSELF TO ENSURE THAT THIS WAR ENDS NOW.
FWAASSH

--AND I'LL BE YOUR WARDEN.
NO!
YOU WON'T KEEP ME HERE, KAL-EL!
YOU CAN'T--
WHAT?
YOU'RE RIGHT, FATHER. SUPERMAN WON'T BE KEEPING AN EYE ON YOU--

--I WILL.
CHRIS?!
THARA AND I FULFILLED OUR ROLES, CLARK. OUR DESTINIES. OUR REUNION FREED THE NIGHTWING AND THE FLAMEBIRD FOR ETERNITY.
SOON THE NIGHTWING WILL LEAVE HERE TO REUNITE WITH THE FLAMEBIRD AND SEAL THE ZONE SHUT PERMANENTLY.
IT'S GRANTED ME ONE LAST WISH, THOUGH...
...THE ABILITY TO SEND YOU HOME.
HUMANKIND NEEDS SUPERMAN. ESPECIALLY GIVEN WHAT LIES AHEAD.
NO! I WON'T LEAVE YOU HERE, NOT WITH ZOD!
DON'T WORRY. THE NIGHTWING WILL MAKE SURE ZOD DOESN'T HARM ANYONE EVER AGAIN.
NOW GO, CLARK!
...NOT SURE...HOW LONG...I CAN HOLD THE PORTAL OPEN!
CHRIS, I CAN'T LOSE YOU AGAIN. I CAN'T!
IT'S GOING TO BE OKAY.
GIVE MY LOVE TO MOM.
NO! CHRIS--!

...CHRIS...
"IT'S OVER."
MY FATHER WAS A COP AND A GOOD MAN AND THIS IS WHAT HE DESERVES.
JONATHAN DREW, YOU ARE UNDER ARREST FOR THE MURDER OF JAMES HARPER, AS WELL AS PARTICIPATING IN THE GENOCIDE OF THE KRYPTONIAN PEOPLE...
"...YOU HAVE THE RIGHT TO REMAIN SILENT..."
C:>//DAILYPLANET/securelogin/loislane
They called it "The Hundred Minute War."
Following the destruction of their planet...
...upwards of twenty thousand Kryptonians--led by General Zod--attacked the Earth...
...and in just under two hours they were repelled.
Both sides suffered terrible losses...

...both human...
SAMUEL L
LANE
IOWA
GENERAL OF
YOU DIN'T BRING **FLOWERS**, MISS?

NO. DAD DIDN'T LIKE FLOWERS...

...AND FRANKLY, HE DOESN'T DESERVE THEM.

...and *Kryptonian*.

Several metahumans were responsible for stopping General Zod's attempted destruction of the planet Earth, and yet...

...not all of them can be *accounted* for.
METROPOLIS. SCIENCE POLICE HEADQUARTERS
(STILL UNDER RECONSTRUCTION).
Dear New Control – I'm done. Good luck. Have this as a flower pot. –J
YOU SURE YOU WANT TO LEAVE METROPOLIS, UNCLE JIM?
I CAME HERE TO BRING DREW TO JUSTICE. I STAYED TO HELP CONTROL. DONE AND DONE.
ARE YOU SURE ABOUT LEAVING WITH ME AND GWEN, BILLI?
I CAME HERE FOR YOU AND STAYED FOR MON-EL.
SO DONE AND DONE, TOO, I GUESS, HUH?
ER, NOT QUITE.
YOU ARE LEAVING METROPOLIS
UNCLE JIM?
YES, BILLI?
I'M PREGNANT.
THE PHANTOM ZONE.
CHRIS. HEY BUDDY. BOY, AM I GLAD I FOUND YOU.
BOY'S THE WORD, MON. LOOK AT ME.
YOU REMEMBER MUCH?
SOME. SUPERMAN. ZOD AND THE NIGHTWING. I'M TRYING TO KEEP THE MEMORY OF THARA, BUT IT'S ALL SLIPPING AWAY A LITTLE AT A TIME.
THE PHANTOM ZONE DOES THAT.
WHERE ARE WE, ANYWAY?
HONESTLY, I'M NOT SURE. I'VE NEVER BEEN TO THIS PART OF THE ZONE BEFORE.
BUT HEY, IF WE'RE LOST, AT LEAST WE'RE LOST TOGETHER. COME ON...
...MAYBE WE'LL FIND A PLACE IN HERE THAT ISN'T QUITE SO GRAY.
Where they all ended up is a mystery to solve another day.
As for today...

...today is about *healing.*
DID YOU WATCH THE NEWS?
YEAH. THEY'RE PAINTING MY FATHER AS A **HERO**. THE MAN WHO WAS PREPARED FOR THE KRYPTONIANS' "INEVITABLE ATTACK."
WE LOST A **WORLD** OF **PEOPLE** BECAUSE OF HIS PARANOIA, LOIS. HIS FEARS.
HAVE YOU FOUND ANY OF YOUR **PEOPLE**? SURVIVORS?
SUPERBOY PUT HUNDREDS OF ZOD'S MEN IN THE ZONE BEFORE THE PROJECTOR WAS DESTROYED, AND I'VE SEARCHED THE EARTH TWICE OVER. IF ANY KRYPTONIANS **ARE** STILL OUT THERE...
...THEY DON'T WANT TO BE FOUND.
WHAT ARE YOU GOING TO WRITE, LOIS? ABOUT YOUR FATHER?
THE **SAME** THING I ALWAYS WRITE: THE **TRUTH**. THE WORLD NEEDS TO **KNOW** WHAT HE DID.
WHAT ARE **YOU** GOING TO DO, CLARK?
THE SAME THING **I** ALWAYS DO. HELP THOSE WHO NEED IT. MOURN THOSE WE LOST.
MY AUNT... UNCLE ZOR... NAR...
WE LOST SO **MANY**, LOIS. SO MANY PEOPLE WHO COULD'VE HELPED OUR WORLDS.
My father-in-law once told me that the only constant in life is change.
I KNOW, CLARK. AND I'M SORRY.
Change affects us all in different ways, and sometimes we lose sight of what's important. Sometimes we can't let go of the *old* ways of life.
One Kryptonian came to Earth and helped make it a better place.
I'M SO, SO SORRY.
100,000 Kryptonians came and they were seen as a threat. They were met with suspicion, hatred, and eventually, death.
We made him our greatest hero.
We--humanity--were *incapable* of accepting what they had to offer, accepting that change, so we lashed out at them. Destroyed them.

Someday I hope humankind will be more receptive to change, to living as a "melting pot" of people and cultures.
To set aside suspicions and live *together* peacefully.
Sometimes that seems like an *impossible* goal.
For now, though, all we can do is hold *on* to that hope…
…and let the dream for a better world sustain us.
THE END

LOIS LANE!!!
THIS ISN'T HOW I EXPECTED TO SPEND TODAY.

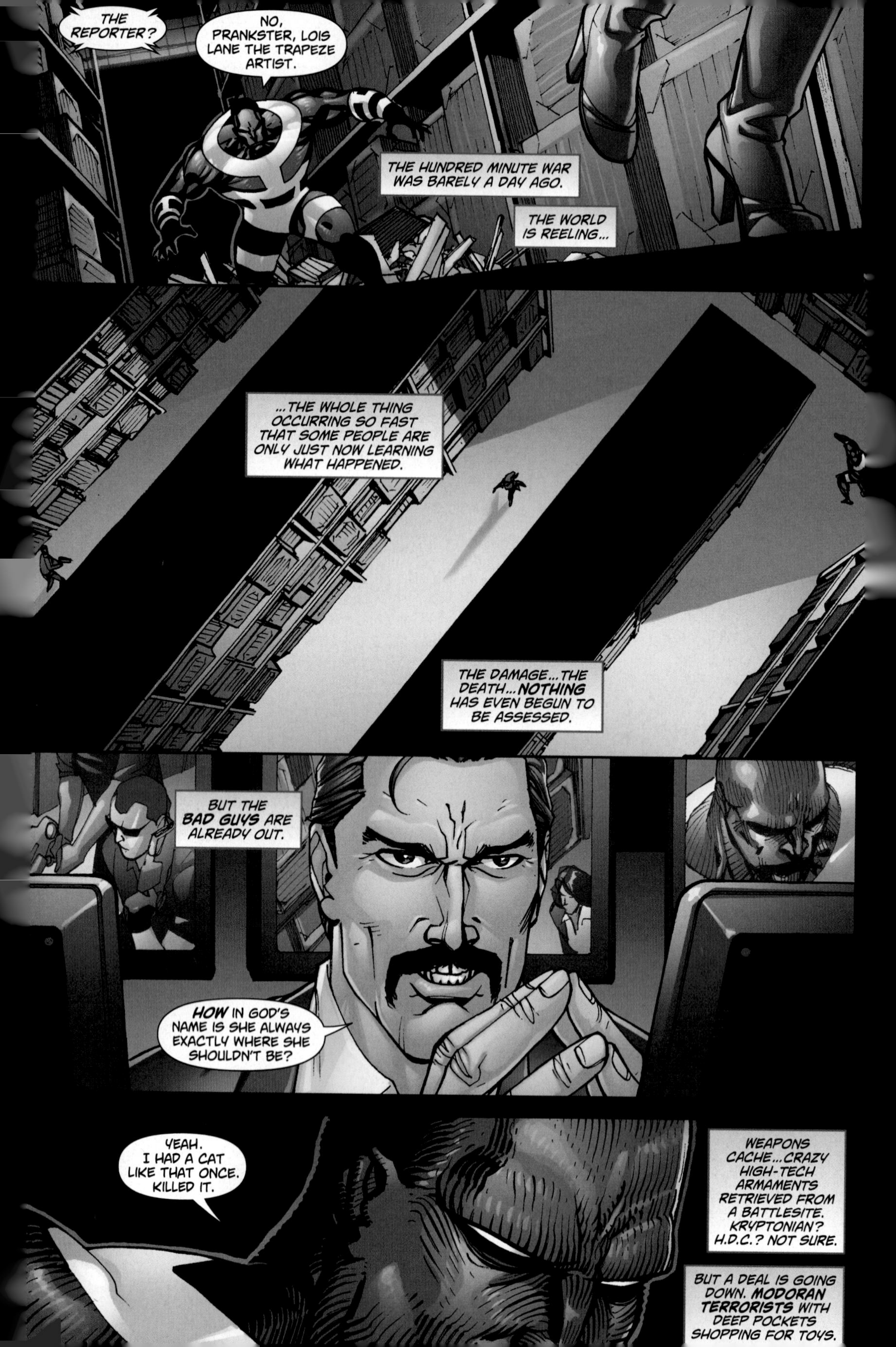
THE REPORTER?
NO, PRANKSTER, LOIS LANE THE TRAPEZE ARTIST.
THE HUNDRED MINUTE WAR WAS BARELY A DAY AGO.
THE WORLD IS REELING...
...THE WHOLE THING OCCURRING SO FAST THAT SOME PEOPLE ARE ONLY JUST NOW LEARNING WHAT HAPPENED.
THE DAMAGE...THE DEATH...NOTHING HAS EVEN BEGUN TO BE ASSESSED.
BUT THE BAD GUYS ARE ALREADY OUT.
HOW IN GOD'S NAME IS SHE ALWAYS EXACTLY WHERE SHE SHOULDN'T BE?
YEAH. I HAD A CAT LIKE THAT ONCE. KILLED IT.
WEAPONS CACHE...CRAZY HIGH-TECH ARMAMENTS RETRIEVED FROM A BATTLESITE. KRYPTONIAN? H.D.C.? NOT SURE.
BUT A DEAL IS GOING DOWN. MODORAN TERRORISTS WITH DEEP POCKETS SHOPPING FOR TOYS.

WELL, HURRY UP AND PRETEND SHE'S YOUR CAT ALL OVER AGAIN, WILL YOU?
PRANKSTER'S THE VENDOR. PARASITE'S THE HIRED MUSCLE.
MY CLIENTS' PLANE LEAVES AT 2:30.
ON IT.
I GET OUT OF THIS, GET MY FINDINGS TO THE POLICE AND MY STORY TO THE PLANET, THEY'LL BOTH GO BACK TO STRYKER'S.

BUT NO...
...OUTRUNNING A PARASITIC PSYCHOPATH ISN'T CLOSE TO HOW I THOUGHT I'D BE SPENDING MY DAY.
HONESTLY...

...I HOPED I'D SEE "HIM" TODAY.
THAT AFTER ALL OUR TIME APART, ALL WE'VE GONE THROUGH, AND ULTIMATELY ALL WE'VE BOTH LOST...

...TODAY. AFTER THE WAR... THE WAR AND THE DEATH AND THE SAD, TERRIBLE TRAGEDY OF IT ALL...
...I'D HOPED THAT AT LEAST I'D SEE HIM AGAIN.

OH!

HELLO, MS. LANE.
IT'S BEEN A WHILE.

THOUGHT YOU WERE GONE, SUPERMAN! NO MATTER!
WHEN I'M DONE WITH YOU, YOU'LL--
--WISH I NEVER CAME BACK?
YEAH, I'M SURE YOU WON'T BE THE LAST VILLAIN TO SAY THAT, EITHER.

TROUBLE IS...

NNNNN

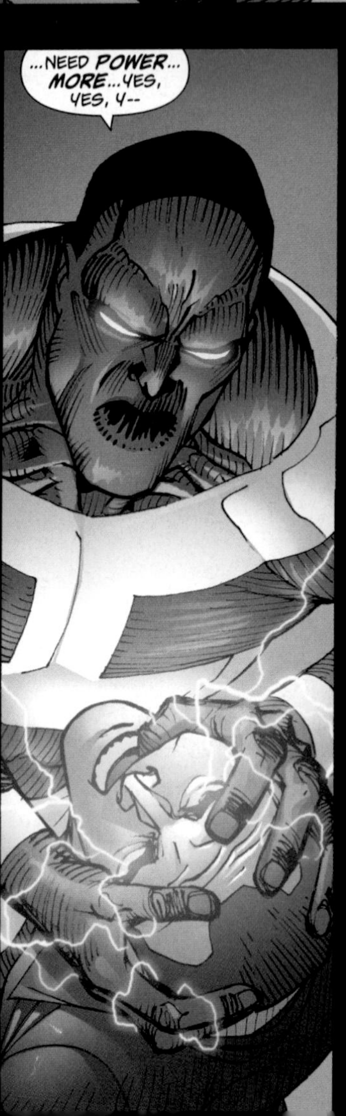
...NEED POWER... MORE...YES, YES, Y--

...TROUBLE FOR GUYS LIKE YOU, THAT IS...
G--
...THERE'S TOO MUCH HERE IN METROPOLIS FOR ME TO LEAVE IT FOREVER.

YEAH...

...THERE'S TOO MUCH HERE I CARE ABOUT.

LATER. VILLAINS JAILED AND STORY FILED.
I DON'T WANT TO TALK ABOUT IT, BABY. I CAN'T.
IT WAS TOO HORRIBLE. MY DAD...THE GUN... SEEING HIM TAKE HIS LIFE...
I CAN'T EVEN IMAGINE WHAT YOU WENT THROUGH. KRYPTON. MY GOD!
LOIS, I--IF I THINK ABOUT EVERYTHING...ALL THAT WAS LOST. ALL THAT COULD HAVE BEEN.
IF I ALLOW MYSELF TO DWELL ON THAT FOR EVEN A MOMENT--
COME HERE.
LOIS...MY TIME AWAY FROM YOU...WHAT I HAD TO DO.
THE THOUGHT OF YOU WAS ALL THAT KEPT ME GOING.

AND THEN HOME.

SO WHAT NOW?

AS IN?
AS IN EVERYTHING. I DON'T KNOW WHAT I'M ASKING, HONESTLY. AFTER ALL THAT'S HAPPENED... AND NOW YOU WITH ME AGAIN, FINALLY. MY MIND'S A BLUR--
WELL...

...IF YOU MEAN METROPOLIS AND THE WORLD, WE'LL REBUILD AND HONOR OUR FALLEN HEROES.
OR IF YOU MEAN US, CLARK KENT WILL RETURN FROM HIS LEAVE OF ABSENCE FROM THE DAILY PLANET AND YOU AND ME WILL GO BACK TO BEING YOU AND ME.

OR DO YOU MEAN SHOULD WE CALL OUT FOR ITALIAN OR CHINESE?... IN WHICH CASE, I VOTE ITALIAN.

LOIS.
BABY?
CHRIS SAVED ME.
AND NOW WE'VE LOST HIM AGAIN.

HE'S ALIVE, CLARK. HOLD ON TO HOPE. YOU TAUGHT ME THAT.
WE'LL SEE HIM AGAIN, I KNOW IT.

I CAN'T STOP KISSING YOU.
AND I HOPE YOU NEVER DO, MISTER.

CAN WE GO OUT?
DINNER?
I'M NOT REALLY HUNGRY, HONESTLY. NO...

...OUT!
I NEVER FEEL CLOSER TO YOU THAN NOW...
...THESE TIMES.
BECAUSE WE'RE ALONE, THE TWO OF US?
BECAUSE IF YOU LET GO OF ME NOW, I'D FALL AND DIE. BUT INSTEAD, YOU'RE HERE AND I'M SAFE.